GRAB THE BROOM, NOT MY BABY

Kristy Prodorutti BScN, MN, RN

ISBN: 978-1-7775072-1-3 (Electronic book)
ISBN: 978-1-7775072-0-6 (Printed book)

Disclaimers: The events in this book are memories from my perspective. All stories that include others' perspectives were used with their permission.

The intention within this work is to include all mothers and parents within their unique situation, no matter what pronoun/gender they choose to identify with, as well, whatever relationship they are in. In certain stories I use my pronouns "she/her", as well as, "my husband" but I acknowledge that not every person identifies in these ways. Efforts were put toward writing in a way that is as inclusive as possible.

Cover designed by Yna
Book designed by Yosua Sirait

First printing edition 2021.

FOR MY LATE GODPARENTS: JOHN AND DIANE

A godparent is a gift sent from above
A guardian angel chosen with love.
As you two lay in your final resting ground,
I feel your presence stronger than ever in my heart,
and all around.
I love you and miss you both.

CONTENTS

A LETTER TO ALL THE NEW MAMAS OUT THERE

Tina Fey once said, "being a mom has made me so tired. And so happy."

I know what you're thinking: out of all of the philosophical and meaningful quotes that exist on the topic of motherhood, I chose to open this book with the wise ol' words of Tina Fey. Pretty deep stuff.

That quote – very much like motherhood itself – may be modest, but it is certainly powerful. It speaks truth to the soul. Though we may not know Tina Fey on a personal level, we can all appreciate her successful career built on a foundation of wholehearted honesty.

So, let's take some inspiration from Tina and use it to cut out some of the bullshit surrounding motherhood; let's talk about the true realities of becoming a mother.

It is hard.

It is exhausting.

Is it wonderful? Abso-friggen-lutely. It's the single most rewarding experience of my life, hands down.

Is it the best thing that has ever happened to me? Without question.

Is it challenging? To say the least.

Messy? Yup.

Life-changing? Well, that's an understatement.

I'm a Registered Nurse that holds my Master's in Nursing and have devoted my career as a nurse to the specialty of Maternity. When I had my first child, Matteo, I felt as though there was no better way to enter into motherhood than to have the knowledge and training that I had. My career helped me immensely; I was a maven at changing diapers, had a pretty respectable understanding about breastfeeding, and could bathe a baby like nobody's business.

But then I became a mother. I started feeling anxious. The relationship with my husband took a turn. I didn't recognize my own body. I missed my extra bubbly self at social events. I didn't have the energy or the same patience for the nonsense that I always seemed to manage before having a child. My house wasn't always ready to be on the cover of a Martha Stewart Living magazine (because this was something I thought could happen at any given moment before becoming a mother), my dog became a third-class citizen, and my husband didn't seem to ever have clean underwear folded neatly in his drawer anymore. On top of it all, no matter how I was feeling on any given day, it was as if I was constantly reminding myself that my old life was gone forever and there was a no-return policy on the life I had traded it in for.

Before having a baby, I had a very clear idea of how motherhood would look on me. It was all so very simple, I would continue to be the exact same person as before. That's it. How hard could it be? When I realized this was *not possible*, I began to struggle with my identity.

I can tell you, with sincere emotion, that everything my education and career taught me about raising a baby were minuscule compared to the life experience and knowledge gained during that first year of motherhood. I began to wonder, if I really was someone who considered myself an expert in all-things-babies and my first year of motherhood was the most significant learning curve I had ever experienced, then how do all new moms feel? I mean, my job is literally preparing families to enter into the world with their newborn and, well, *parent.* So what was it about this "parenting thing" that caught me so off-guard?

After a lot of self-reflection, I began to understand my thoughts and feelings. I was not at all equipped for my personal evolution into motherhood or for my psychosomatic transition into this new — and much more significant and meaningful — life.

All of a sudden, my old self was left on the delivery table in the labour room, right alongside my placenta, and the birth of my baby happened in unison with the birth of my new self. I felt as though giving birth brought life to my new perspective of the world, including a changed outlook, new values, and different priorities. Maintaining my house to a level that I could eat off the floor didn't hold the same importance anymore. And cleaning my husband's dirty underwear slowly made its way down to the very bottom of my priority list.

I then began to witness high rates of postpartum depression and anxiety in many new moms around me. I couldn't believe how many of us were struggling. That is when I knew something about the way we were doing things needed to change.

Much of the research dedicated to postpartum depression and anxiety has found a close link to the societal pressures of perfection and, the totally unattainable, expectations of motherhood. As a society, we have created a myth that portrays motherhood as nothing short of blissful. When we don't find this experience to be true because we aren't excelling perfectly at motherhood, we deem ourselves failures. It is irrational to expect women to morph into flawless mothers overnight without struggle, angst, sadness, or challenges. Along those same lines, mothers have become more and more isolated from our communities; which means not only are we supposed to do things perfectly, but we are supposed to *do it all* perfectly.

With this in mind, I started journaling, researching, and brainstorming strategies that would support all mothers to become more resilient and mentally healthy during the very challenging first year of motherhood and, in turn, for the rest of their lives.

It's time to transform our communities. We must talk about raw truths of motherhood, share our stories to help prepare mothers-to-be to the best of their ability, break down the expectations of perfection, find and create support in our communities, and construct a world that helps mothers take better care of their babies by focusing on better care for themselves.

Here is my journey. Here are my struggles. Here are my learning curves. And here I am to present my strategies to help you and your beautiful family stay healthy mentally, emotionally, physically, and spiritually. I hope when you read this it puts a smile on your face, confidence in your mind, and strength in your soul. Enjoy.

Kristy P.

1. MAKING SENSE OF MATERNAL MENTAL HEALTH

Is What We're Feeling Normal?

LET'S start this chapter off with some hard-core truth: virtually **all women** have the potential to develop a mood disorder during pregnancy or within the first year after delivery.[1] No woman is entirely and wholly protected from the physiological, emotional, and psychological changes that accompany life after having a baby.

Unfortunately, there is no limit to the confusing societal messages that are consistently creating the illusion that parenthood should only be associated with feelings of happiness. We anticipate feelings of elation, overwhelming joy, and harmony as we raise our babies. Of course, there *is* joy in bringing a life into this world! Babies are nothing short of a blessing, so why would we feel anything other than over-the-moon? But the constant messages emphasizing parenting as entirely a joyful event validates the belief that feelings of sorrow, experienced at any stage of the birth of a child, is considered an abnormal response that is *an individual flaw to be fixed.*[2] Essentially, we are taught that motherhood and bad feelings do not mix. Ever. So, when sadness starts creeping up on us and we cry for no apparent reason, we may feel a little caught off-guard—to say the least.

The truth is, although we may imagine mothering to be an instinctual ability that we hold deep inside of us, it is still a journey of lifelong learning. There are days we question our capabilities, days we lose confidence in ourselves, days we struggle to perform effortlessly, and days we feel unfavourable emotions even when they are logically unwarranted.

This is natural.

So, what am I really supposed to feel, you ask? How do I know when these bad feelings are too much? Where is the line between the normal struggles of motherhood versus a perinatal mood disorder that I may be suffering from? Great questions!

Let's explore...

BABY BLUES

There is a physiologic and hormonal adjustment period that occurs after you have given birth to your beautiful baby. Your body selflessly created life, nourished it, and then brought it into this world, so let's give it a little time to recover, people! The hormonal regulation is simply your body recuperating from its overwhelming duty of producing that perfect little bundle. It formed your baby's ten little toes, sculpted that perfect button nose, and built a set of lungs; now it's back to the more mundane role of simply keeping you alive. Easy, right?

After the momentous task of creating life, your body is just a tad exhausted and it has lost some focus, so the recovery period can be a little shaky. This is not the time to hold high expectations over yourself regarding what you should be "in control" of during this stage of motherhood. So, yes, during this time you have a free pass to cry just for the hell of it at any given moment. Here are some quick facts:

Baby blues is not a medical condition.

Baby blues only lasts up to two weeks after delivery.

Baby blues does not require an intervention.

It does, of course, require the support and understanding of those around us to make sure our feelings remain within the normalcy of postpartum and does not develop into anything further. However, baby blues is *not* an interchangeable term with postpartum depression or any other perinatal mood disorder for that matter.

Simply put, if getting through the day is seemingly an impossible task for you after two weeks postpartum and you are absolutely debilitated by undesirable feelings, it is time to seek help.

Here is what to know when baby blues has advanced into something more.

PREGNANCY OR POSTPARTUM DEPRESSION

Pregnancy or postpartum depression (PPD) is the most largely talked about diagnosis surrounding motherhood in Western culture and is sometimes used as a blanket term for other perinatal mood disorders, even though it is very specific and separate from other diagnoses. During pregnancy, and even more commonly within six to eight weeks after delivery, most healthcare providers will routinely screen mothers for PPD using a specific tool called the Edinburgh Postnatal Depression Scale

(Appendix A). Though a slight range of prevalence is found among studies, it is recognized that approximately 15% of mothers experience clinical depression during pregnancy or succeeding the birth of their child, though I am certain many cases go undiagnosed.

It is important to note that symptoms are subjective and individualistic; however, common feelings associated with PPD are:

- A lack of interest in your baby
- Immense irritability or anger
- Crying and sadness that have surpassed the first two weeks after your delivery, including feelings of hopelessness, strong guilt, or shame
- Changes in appetite (overeating or a loss of appetite)
- Sleep disturbances (brought on by your thoughts, not because you're woken up by your baby that needs to feed)
- Loss of pleasure or interest in things that you used to enjoy doing or being a part of
- Thoughts of causing harm to yourself or your baby[3]

Even though we are essentially all at risk, certain factors link individuals to a higher likelihood of developing PPD. These include, but are not limited to, a traumatic delivery experience, an unwanted pregnancy, being a teen mom or a mother of multiples, a previous diagnosis of depression, thyroid imbalance or diabetes, having an unsupportive partner or family, living in poverty, migration, extreme stress including a major life event, and exposure to violence (domestic, sexual, and gender-based).[4]

Funnily enough, we don't understand as much about PPD as we think we do. While some researchers believe PPD is a specific pathological reaction to childbirth, others consider a more holistic approach, which has led to inconsistency and controversy surrounding PPD.[5]

PPD has been a topic of discussion as far back as the era of Hippocrates. During this time in history, this diagnosis was believed to be caused by the function of lactation. It was our body's response to our milk production and an indication for the "problems" following childbirth; this phenomenon was known as milk fever.[6] In addition, there has been a multitude of research focused on understanding the neurobiology of PPD and emphasizing the use of medications to "fix" the chemical makeup of a mother's brain.[7]

But if we focus solely on the physiological processes of PPD, why, then, do psychosocial factors, such as experiencing hardships, also put one at greater risk of this diagnosis? Just by reviewing the list of the risk factors, it is clear that *PPD is multifaceted;* there are so many pieces to the puzzle that can lead to these less than desirable feelings in a mother during pregnancy or after delivering a baby. To even further recognize the complexities within a PPD diagnosis, there is research that confirms fathers can also experience postpartum depression. That means more discussion around an individual's experience is necessary for a greater understanding of this diagnosis.[8]

What I find interesting is, globally, communities that view the postpartum period as a time for community support, instead of individual responsibility, are associated with fewer incidences of PPD. With a minimal focus on pharmacological treatment, symptoms are viewed more so as a product of societal or environmental factors (such as poverty or lack of support as mentioned above).[9] Instead of looking introspectively at the mother and asking, "What is wrong with her?", it's important to look outwards and ask, "As a community what are we doing, or not doing, that is causing the mother to feel this way and how can we make things better for her?" When viewed in such a way, we can recognize community support as a normal aspect in the postpartum period and that taking care of our youth is a shared responsibility; something for all of us to think about...

PREGNANCY OR POSTPARTUM ANXIETY

It may seem as though postpartum depression takes the cake on a hierarchy of mood disorders. Due to improving awareness of mental health, our communities have begun to show empathy toward people living with PPD. This is great news, but I feel as though we have a little more ways to go on the topic of anxiety. Those suffering from postpartum anxiety (PPA) often don't receive the same amount of sympathy, maybe due to a lack of true understanding of such a diagnosis. It is important to recognize that anxiety and depression can be experienced as simply one or the other, can be experienced simultaneously, or feelings of one can morph into feelings of the other. And, although there is some overlap within our depressive screening tools for anxiety, there is room for growth to properly screen and identify PPA the same we do for PPD. In turn, we must understand that **living with an anxiety disorder is just as devastating as living with depression.**

It is believed that roughly 10% of women develop anxiety during pregnancy or within the first year after delivery. However, just like PPD, I can assume that many cases are undiagnosed, or symptoms of anxiety are misinterpreted as a depression diagnosis. One study that dove deep into postpartum anxiety research brought light to our ignorance surrounding PPA when a mother explained that she, "felt like [her feelings] must be postpartum depression... because that's the only sort of term [she] could come up with that was something."[10] These thoughts clearly emphasize the fact we tend to use PPD as the blanket term for all mood disorders, and the opportunity for improvement in relation to our understanding of different diagnoses in the perinatal period.

There is a purpose to anxiety; it's an innate feeling to keep us safe by creating a reaction in our bodies that will serve to protect us and remove us from danger. But let's delve into what takes PPA out of the regular realm of worry into a perinatal mood disorder diagnosis.

The most common feelings of PPA:

- Severe and constant worries and fears (often related to the health and safety of your baby)
- A persistent uneasiness that something bad is going to happen
- Racing thoughts
- Thoughts about death (fearing death due to perceived danger)
- Changes in appetite (overeating or a loss of appetite)
- Sleep disturbances (brought on by thoughts, not because you are being woken by your baby that needs to feed)
- Inability to sit still
- Dizziness
- Hot flashes
- Nausea[11]

Just as with PPD, there are certain risk factors linked to higher incidences of PPA. These include recent stressful life events, relationship problems, unrealistic expectations of motherhood by the woman or others around her, lack of social support, pregnancy complications, and infant health problems.[12]

Mental health is profound and it does not end at a basic understanding of PPD and PPA; it's much more complicated than that. **Included at the back of this book is more information on other types of perinatal mood disorder specifics including postpartum psychosis, postpartum anxiety disorders: panic attacks, obsessive compulsive disorder and post-traumatic stress disorder, as well as resources if you feel the need to seek out help. If this interests you, please turn to page 189.**

To diagnose a perinatal mood disorder is not as straightforward as getting an x-ray on our arm to confirm that it's broken after we fall on it. Our environment, genetic makeup, situational circumstances, friends and family, exposures and experiences, and coping abilities all play a part in our mental health. We only receive a diagnosis with in-depth assessments and an explanation of the sufferer's symptoms. To make matters even more complex, the stigma surrounding mental health creates an environment that a sufferer may not be completely honest in order to avoid a diagnosis. That said, it's imperative we acknowledge when our symptoms have surpassed normalcy and are affecting our life more than necessary. If so, we must seek out help and support no matter what point we are at in our journey.

So, where do we go from here?

Well, this knowledge is, essentially, our first step toward healing and resiliency! Knowing that there *is* a normalcy of symptoms that can be somewhat undesirable in motherhood is an important message I feel compelled to share. In turn, I want the discourse of motherhood to change in a way that reflects those unwarranted tears, unexpected undesirable feelings, and some of the sadness that comes along for the ride. I want to be one small voice who shares my journey that is full of the lessons I learned intending to help you grab motherhood by the balls and power through it like the warrior I know you are. We don't need to wait until our feelings become unbearable before we give our mental health some love. *Prevention is just as important as treatment*. So, no matter where you are at with your journey let's dive in and learn about how we can create a lifestyle full of strategies and an approach to motherhood that helps us live our best lives in the most healthy way possible.

2.

YOU ARE NEW AND IMPROVED... EMBRACE IT!

Life, as you Know it, is Forever Changed

WHEN you become a mother, your life will never be the same. Before you get frightened by these words, run away from motherhood, and never look back, know that this is not a warning. Read those words again. Life will never be the same; *life will be better.*

Yes, life will be hard. Life will be much more work. Life will be tiring, challenging, full of worry, and sometimes overwhelming. Yet, life will also be deeply rewarding. Motherhood will give you a sense of fulfillment. You will become so full of gratitude for the life you created, your heart will grow ten sizes bigger, just like in a Doctor Seuss book.

I was once told that when you're making any type of significant transition in life, there is always something that you will be letting go of. Big or small, whatever it may be, you will need to take the time to mourn that loss. **But if you are moving in the right direction, then the benefit of what's to come will be more significant than whatever it is you're giving up.**

Transitioning into motherhood does mean the loss of certain things. I, for one, mourned the loss of staying in bed on Saturdays until three in the afternoon. I mourned the loss of peacefully drinking a *hot* coffee during breakfast on my porch with my husband, Ryan. I also, in vain, mourned the loss of my perky boobs. It's okay to feel as though you've lost a part of yourself. Because the fact is, you have. You have lost a juvenile and young version of yourself and you have replaced it with a mature version that comes with unimaginable maternal instincts and big important responsibilities. Now you're living to protect and nurture another human being, and to me, that is a much better version. You can replace your peaceful hot coffee in the morning with an exciting, chaotic breakfast full of smiles and giggles, watching your baby grow right before your eyes.

After entering motherhood, believing that I could be the same person as I was before giving birth was one of the biggest instigators behind some of the angst I experienced in my first year of motherhood; a feeling I had a hard time comprehending. I felt the need to be exactly who I was for everyone in my life, especially for my husband. He married a younger version of me, so I didn't think it was fair to morph into someone entirely different overnight. Looking back on my pregnancy (and even the first few weeks after my delivery) I truly believed that I could be the same person and manage life the way I had for the last 30 years. When I was about to enter into motherhood, I imagined some toys neatly organized in the corner of my ultra-modern living room and a highchair around my sleek, fingerprint-free glass kitchen table, but other than that my house would still be the same, right? I imagined my boobs would fluctuate in size from breastfeeding, but other than that my body would look and feel the same, right? Oh, and I knew I would get a little less sleep, but I would still have just as much patience and energy for everyone in my life, right? Wrong.

Wrong. Wrong. Wrong.

And wrong to everything else in my life that I thought would remain unchanged. Everything was different and once I couldn't recognize myself anymore, I started plummeting into a spiral of distress. I didn't know how to navigate this foreign land of what was now my new life, as a new human being. Like a pilot losing control of her plane, I began my nosedive, having no skills or experience to gain back control and save myself from a crash landing.

There were a handful of instances over the course of a few months in the postpartum period that brought about alarming feelings within me that I had never felt before. I experienced one episode followed by another and then another. That triggered my fear of having these episodes non-stop. More deeply, it triggered a fear in me that I was no longer in control of my life, my emotions, or my thoughts. It was then I knew I had to find a way to understand where these feelings were coming from.

I want to acknowledge that my experiences I chose to share may not look, sound, or feel like anything you have encountered in your parenting journey and it may not make any sense to you whatsoever, but that's the uniqueness of mental health. It's never a one-size-fits-all subject. I share these stories with the consideration that I am only one perspective.

My first intense experience was brought about by nothing more than a friend's birthday party. That's right, a birthday party. Matteo was about eight weeks old and I was worried about leaving him for a good portion of the night; I questioned if I had enough bottles of breast milk pumped for him and if he would fall asleep without me there. But to all my girlfriends, I screamed my excitement from the rooftops, overjoyed about a girl's night out. I played it cool like I had things all figured out as a brand-new mom, not a care in the world.

It was time to partyyy!

The day of the birthday party didn't play out exactly as planned, which truly is no different than any other day with an infant. Naps weren't taken on time, Matteo decided this was a day he wanted to clusterfeed, other family obligations happened, and the list went on and on. We had dinner plans at this new trendy restaurant in town with a very strict reservation policy. I was told well in advance our party wouldn't be seated until all the guests arrived, and I was responsible to pick up another friend on the way downtown. As time was creeping up on me, I knew I was going to be late. Before leaving the house, already behind schedule, I needed to breastfeed *just one more time* and Matteo needed to make an explosion in his diaper a few more times after that. Matteo was not settling as I tried to head out the door and, all of a sudden, my insides felt like a can of Pepsi that had been in the back of a pickup truck on a bumpy road. I looked at my husband who asked me if I was okay and, just like slightly cracking the lid to a shaken bottle of soda, my emotions exploded. Within this very confusing eruption, I was a mess. I was full of fear, unpreparedness, anger, and guilt. I felt unprepared to leave my baby and that feeling, in turn, brought about an overwhelming fear that something bad was going to happen to Matteo if I did.

I felt guilt for everyone involved. Guilty for letting my friends down who were counting on me to be at the birthday party on time and for my husband, who was also a new parent, dealing with a side of his wife that he has never seen on top of being left to be responsible for our son alone, although he was very capable. I felt particularly guilty that I was prioritizing a birthday party over my perfect baby boy cuddled in my arms. I also felt a lot of anger. Though I didn't understand it at the time, I was mad at myself for having an out-of-control reaction to something as trivial as a birthday party. Luckily, I was surrounded by a lot of support that helped me make it out that night and we all lived to tell the tale. Matteo was just fine with Daddy and no one cared that I was late to the party.

Even so, I remember waking up the next morning feeling as though I had been hit by a bus—and no, it wasn't from the fireball shots that I had the night prior. Confused about all of my feelings from the previous day, I decided to spend some time journaling. The previous night felt particularly significant because it appeared to be a trivial event, yet it led to me feeling as though the world was going to end. I realized it really wasn't the birthday party that got me to the place I found myself in; what got me there were the expectations of the night that I held onto so firmly. More specifically, it was the expectation that I had put on myself – the idea that I could continue to navigate life in the same manner that I had managed before becoming a mom. However, after becoming responsible for another human being, life didn't feel so straightforward anymore. I needed to reassess my priorities to get myself to a place that supported my transition into motherhood.

Another episode happened when Matteo was about ten weeks old. My sweet husband planned a spontaneous date night for the two of us. Though his heart was in the right place, arranging a babysitter, having Matteo's bag packed and bottles pumped within a matter of minutes, absolutely put me over the edge. Yet again, I felt completely overwhelmed and inundated with fear, guilt, and anger. In the same breath, I felt the need to prevail because I didn't want to let my husband down. Needless to say, when we dropped Matteo off at the babysitters and went on our date, I had a complete and utter meltdown.

At the time, I never told Ryan how overwhelmed I felt as a new mother. I told him that my Caesarian section incision hurt because, as a man, he understood physical pain. Physical pain made total sense for the tears pouring down my cheeks. I had major surgery and a scar to prove it, so that was my excuse. I never wanted to explain to him why I couldn't handle such spontaneity during this period in our lives (though I love him for being so thoughtful), or our very hectic and demanding social life because those were the people we were and our life had always been so wonderful. I didn't want him to see me as boring, weak, high maintenance, nor someone who couldn't do it all. I had always managed to do it all and *that* is the person he wanted to marry, right?

Just as I had felt the day after my friend's birthday party, the next day after our date night, I felt hit by that same dang bus again! This was the moment that I decided to speak to my husband about how I was feeling. I told him I was changing, my priorities were different, my mind was different, and I needed to take the time to figure out how to make changes in my life to reflect who I was as a mother. Do you know what he told me?

"Of course you do."

It was that simple and he truly meant it. Life, as we knew it to be, was forever changed and he did his best to support my evolution into motherhood, but it was up to me to be vocal about how I was feeling and what I needed. I now tell him when our hectic schedule is making me feel overwhelmed or when rest, or Matteo cuddles, is the priority over a birthday party. I also tell him when we need to order take-out for dinner because I just can't manage cooking that day or if I need his help to fold the laundry. Even now, a year later, Ryan still checks in with me about how I'm managing things and he never tries to put expectations on me. Though I feel we have made huge strides in our parenting journey, we continue to learn to navigate our new normal as a family.

So, you ask, have I taken all those birthday parties and date nights with my husband off the table? Absolutely not! Socialization remains very important to me. I still find time for those date nights, nights with my friends, and a little time away from Matteo while balancing what works for my family and what works for me. However, my life's priority list has been altered and looks and feels different than it has in the past. It just took some time for me to understand it.

I, too, had to recognize Ryan's transition into fatherhood, which was a journey independent from mine. We were living the experience together, but our feelings weren't always in unison. For many fathers – or any parent for that matter – it can take much longer than anticipated to synchronize their priorities to their new life. Be cognizant that experiences are personal. Don't believe you and your significant other will be holding hands and skipping through the roses together during this life-altering time in your journey. Make sure you receive respect for your evolution and give respect to your partner for experiencing it their way, *on their own time.*

As it went for my husband, he began to feel more like a father when he was given specific responsibilities to care for Matteo. It was so important for Ryan to be involved in feeding the pumped bottles of milk I had stored and even more important to participate in Matteo's swimming lessons around four months old; those were the times he shined as a dad. We need to be sensitive to the parts we are solely responsible for, as mothers or as the birth parent, which may leave the other parent feeling inadequate such as the pregnancy, the labour, the delivery, and breastfeeding. I think I named a few important roles there, don't you? So how can we support our significant others to find their involvement within their parenthood evolution? Maybe it's swimming lessons, bath time, storytime, or feeding them their first solid foods.

For me to be completely transparent with you, I want you to understand that our transition as a married couple into parenthood was not as simple as just having one conversation that set in stone how our new world is, and will always be. Every now and again, we slip back into our old ways. I told you I was going to speak raw truth, so I don't want to sugarcoat this: our first year of parenthood was *hands down* the hardest year of our relationship and we've been together for over 15 years. I didn't think we could have been more prepared or have a stronger foundation than the life my husband and I had created together. We experienced our teen years together, high school, and all of our 20s, university, moving out, homeownership, pets, and losing loved ones. We've traveled, gotten into trouble, drank too much, partied too much, learned thousands of lessons together the hard way, and I thought that having a baby was just one more notch on the list of our experiences. But having Matteo shook our foundation a thousand times greater than anything else we had been through and more than I could have ever imagined. Regardless, we continue to work through this new life together. We will continue to work harder than ever to improve our communication, support each other's needs, and evolve both individually and as a couple to persevere through the rocky times.

I hope that every one of you reading this today has a support system or significant other who welcomes your evolution into motherhood, just as my husband has. More importantly, I hope that *you* accept it too. Allow yourself to transition and allow your significant other to transition all in their own right. Enjoy it. Embrace it. Don't fight it. And be proud of the new and improved version of yourself.

YOU WOULD BE SURPRISED HOW MANY MOTHERS FEEL THE SAME AS YOU OR ARE GOING THROUGH THE SAME THINGS

—**Courtney S.**
Mom to Abigail and Gareth

3

WHO'S IN YOUR MAMA CREW?

Finding a Support System

THE modern-day North American lifestyle can be luxurious, superficial, and self-centred. Along the same lines, it can lead to a very isolating existence. Though we may not notice how desolate we truly are, there are experiences in life that prove the need for a supportive community around us. Having a baby is one of those experiences.

My advice? Find yourself a community of mothers. I wish I could surround these words with blinking lights, sparklers, and a little pop of glitter to highlight their importance.

Unlike the sparkle and glitter surrounding these words, motherhood is not always so attractive. Unfortunately, and I have heard this far too many times, many new moms feel extremely isolated. Now, this isn't to say they don't have a supportive mother, in-laws, friends, or co-workers that care deeply, but many times they don't have people in their corner they can truly relate to. You know, someone that is actually living it, in the trenches, just as they are. Someone who's also experiencing those sleepless nights, constantly smelling like spit-up, and leaking breast milk through their shirt just at the mere thought of their baby. Even more, to have someone that doesn't make them feel like they are completely insane for texting a picture of a dirty diaper to ask if their infant's poop is supposed to look exactly like Dijon mustard.

I am sure your mother can often be that voice of reason when you need her, but she also, for the majority of us, isn't raising a baby of her own in the world *today*. Even if she is still an absolute ace at feeding a bottle and getting your baby to settle from a crying spree, she may not truly understand the struggles of raising a baby in this day-and-age.

Let's get a little deep here for a second while we are on the topic of our mothers. At some point, we may have thought our mother (or parent) was superhuman. We probably now know that they are just, well, human. If you didn't know that, I'm sorry to be the bearer of bad news. That's okay though because now you may understand that they, too, made mistakes. You don't have to be perfect to survive parenthood. Let's pick out how our parents excelled at raising us and drop certain things that we may not completely agree with. Focusing solely on what your parents know about parenting closes our door to evolving, seeking new and updated information, and growing from mistakes in our past. Give them their space in your library of knowledge, but don't allow them to fill all of your shelves. Because we are the by-product of our mothers and fathers, their actions (cognizant or not) are what shapes who we are today. That includes the stress or anxiety they felt and intergenerational trauma that continues to get passed down – meaning we can be affected by violence, abuse, loss, and suffering that previous generations lived through even if we didn't directly experience it. At some point, we need to make room to heal from these attributes. Doing this by seeking out advice from other sources can lead us to become more well-rounded mothers. *Sorry, Mom!* For those reasons, I stress the importance of seeking out other moms who are where you are in your journey.

Now let's get back to it. Is the thought of putting yourself out there to find new friends making you cringe with nerves? Well, let me tell you this: *there are moms everywhere seeking you out too*. You may be thinking that it's not so simple to just round up a bunch of mothers, but they are all over the place! Baby yoga, anyone? What about a new mom's network through your Public Health Agency? If that doesn't sound appealing, how about a visit to your local library where they offer loads of mom-and-baby classes? There are also swimming lessons and stroller-friendly workout classes. There are baby barre classes, Facebook communities, neighbourhood community groups, and walking groups. There are specific classes aimed at different stages of parenthood, such as breastfeeding support groups. I could go on and on. Get creative. What about online forums connecting you to other mothers from all over the world? Online communities can connect us more than ever before. That village we may not feel a part of or, heck, we may not even know who our next-door neighbours are – we now have tools to build our own communities. That is truly a gift.

The first step, then, is to find something that piques your interest. It may be a physical activity like a Baby Bootcamp, a more spiritual encounter like meditation or yoga, or a class that will educate you like a breastfeeding group. The second step: get going and give it a fair shot. Introduce yourself to the group and let the other participants know that you're looking to connect with other moms. It's that simple. I assure you that some, if not most, of the moms in the class will be looking for the exact same thing. If you seek, I promise, you shall find.

When you do find some new moms, start building a rapport. Find a way to reach out: regular text messaging, other communication platforms like social media, Facetime, group chats, or in-person coffee dates. You may be surprised how often conversations can be had. I don't think there was one day in that first year of motherhood that I didn't speak to another new mom. In certain messaging groups — My Wine O'clock Crew, for instance — a typical day consisted of about 101 questions back and forth. What do you do for a clogged duct? Why does my baby sneeze exactly three times at 12:57 pm each day? I think some fresh air would do me well, anyone up for a walk or coffee? I needed them and they needed me.

As a new mother, it's important to surround yourself with people that provide you with the right type of support. For that, I want you to ask yourself the following questions:

1. **Does _________ bring positivity into my life?**

   When I interact with them, do they build me up or tear me down? Do I leave an encounter feeling encouraged or defeated? Are my energy levels drained or recharged? Are they constructive or detrimental to my mental health?

2. **Does _________respect my values?**

   You can most definitely have friendships with those whose values and parenting styles are different from yours; I find a lot of benefit in hearing a multitude of different opinions as this allows me to sift through the information until I find what works best for my family. It is, however, important to feel comfortable to get and give advice without feeling judged. It will only add to your angst if you have reached out to mothers who, in turn, make you feel as if you're doing things the wrong way. Find those mothers that understand who you are and what you stand for.

3. How does _________ support me in my journey?

It's important to feel that your support system is actually *supportive*. Each mother you surround yourself with should bring something special to your world. Maybe Sally is the most experienced mother that always has the best tips and tricks. Maybe you laugh for hours on end with Nicole as you swap stories during your play dates. Maybe Tina is the best listener. It could even be as simple as feeling so comfortable with a friend, you can sit there in silence and breastfeed your babies together. If you ever feel as though Karen just loves to hear the gossip of you and your husband's fight last night so she can run to Suzy with the latest news, then no. Karen is out. Get her off your list and out of your life. Karen is completely defeating the purpose of having a support system. (Please don't block all the Karens in your contacts list just because I said so, only do it if she's actually being a 'Karen'). Comfort, love, experience, and advice are a few examples of what may be significant to you when you spend time with your supporters.

A CHALLENGE FOR YOU

Over the next month, with each encounter you have with someone, write down the qualities they possess that bring significance into your world. Then, ask them to do the same about you and what qualities you bring to the table. Remember, friendship is a two-way street. Do *your* share to make a companionship an enriching exchange,[13] and in turn, you can create substantial and valuable connections. Know the value true friendship can bring to your life.

Who you surround yourself with is reflective of who you are or who you are striving to be. There is research that suggests surrounding yourself with happy people can increase your happiness by 25%.[14] Though it seems hard to visualize a person 25% happier in comparison to their old self, understand that the perspective for that person is different and *that* is what matters. On the other side, negativity can breed negativity. So, I ask you, do you have people in your life that inspire you to be a happier, healthier, and enriched version of yourself?

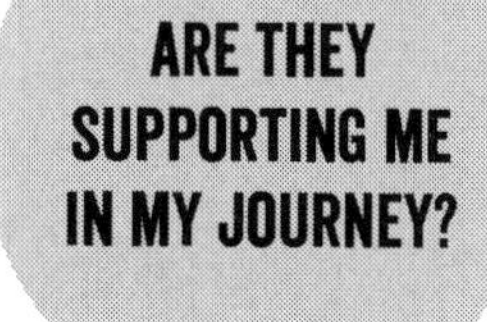

When I started writing this book, I reached out to my mom-friends and asked their advice for a new mom going through the first year of motherhood, knowing what they know

now. Finding a support group of like-minded moms was a unanimous theme. Every single mom I asked had the same answer. Every. Single. Mom.

**Build a support system. Ask lots of questions.
Don't isolate yourself!**

In their ways and through their own stories, these mothers found comfort in other moms. They found someone to talk to, relate to, and connect with. Some mothers told me that it wasn't always a deliberate manhunt to find friends, but as they looked back on their first year of motherhood, they realized how important a role those people played and the immense help they received when they needed it the most. Some said that because of that tough first year together, they created a bond that will last a lifetime.

AND THEN THERE WAS A PANDEMIC

My initial manuscript for this book was written long before COVID-19 took over our world, but now, seeing as though it has cozied up in each crevice and is occupying every square inch of the planet with no intentions of leaving anytime soon, I think it's important to address it in these pages. Now more than ever before, isolation has skyrocketed; it is literally our current way of life for most of us. Not just for us new moms, but especially for us new moms. That said, with our capabilities through Zoom, FaceTime, chat groups, and all other platforms available to us, we can appreciate that these options may help us feel a little less lonely. It may mean that those in-persons support groups aren't running exactly as they were months ago, but there are still a plethora of groups that continue to exist. They just have a slightly altered appearance at the moment. All the strategies that I address in this book are just as important with or without COVID-19. However, it is an example of how certain situations in life can throw us for an unexpected loop and try our resiliency. COVID-19 is another illustration reminding us of the importance of taking care of our mental health. As much as I do not want to give this virus any more of the limelight — because it doesn't deserve any more of our precious time on this Earth — I do feel the need to speak on it. Even though we may not want to acknowledge it, COVID-19 has changed what our world looks like, how we socialize, and how we build relationships, but it does not have to take these things away from us. Our bond with one another is truly an inherent necessity and more vital than ever before.

Research has found that community supports are the most influential factor and most beneficial aspect of treatment for women who are experiencing postpartum depression and postpartum anxiety.[15] So, I am here to tell you that having a community of mothers in your life is not something to just fill your spare time with; Lord knows that mothers don't have spare time. Having a community of mothers in your life is a necessity for you, your mental health, and your baby. Make it a priority. Do not think for one second that you are too busy with a new baby that you don't have time to make new friends. I promise you, we are all busy, and complaining about your busy schedule is the first topic that you can bond over with your new mom crew.

BEING A NEW MOM IS DIFFICULT, BUT IT IS MOST DEFINITELY A BLESSING

-Kara M.

Mom to Kate and Zachary

4
CAN YOU SEE THE RAINBOW?

Seeking out Gratitude

I had a miscarriage.

If you have experienced this, then you understand the weight of those words. *I had a miscarriage.* Many are familiar with the statistics of this event. If you are not, I will tell you that there is about one miscarriage in every four pregnancies. I am also here to tell you this number does not take away the pain of such a loss. One of my doctors told me, "Don't worry, it was just a ball of cells, nothing that mattered." Well, Doc, it mattered to me. It was my baby. My beautiful little nugget with a heartbeat. I saw that heart beating on the ultrasound. *I heard it.*

Every pregnancy is significant; don't let anyone tell you otherwise. The second you pee on that stick and two little lines appear — or a big plus sign or whatever those expensive little gadgets do nowadays: date your pregnancy, flicker, sing to you, throw sparkles into the air — as soon as you find out you are growing a baby inside you, you become a mother. Your world changes. Instinctually you become the most selfless person you have ever been. Every food choice, every bad habit, and every minute of the day you question if this is the right decision for your growing fetus. You download a pregnancy app and open it over and over excited to see what size of fruit your munchkin mimics today. Suddenly your future plans don't seem all that important; that stagette in Vegas, a co-worker's wedding in Mexico, you could probably just do without. Does it work for your pregnancy? Does it work for your baby? If it doesn't, then you scratch it off of your calendar.

You may still mourn the breakup of your favourite happy-hour cocktail, but daydreaming if that little bundle is going to have your nose, or your husband's curly black hair, now that's the best remedy. There is a life-altering feeling in the pit of your stomach that is triggering you to do anything in your power to protect that little "ball of cells".

OUR STORY OF THE BABY WE LOST

My husband and I had just gotten home from a dinner party and, for whatever reason, I felt the need to take a pregnancy test. I didn't think much of it, I just pulled out a stick and peed. Then without a second thought, I tossed it into the trash. I know you must all think I am absolutely nuts, who takes a pregnancy test and doesn't even wait for the results before tossing it? I really can't give you an honest answer. It wasn't the first time I had taken one of those tests and it always ended with the same result, not pregnant. So why would this time be any different? Maybe I didn't want to get my hopes up again. So I peed on the stick and threw it out. Thinking back on it now, there must have been a tiny voice in my head — or maybe in my uterus — telling me to pee on that stick in the first place.

A little while later, as I was brushing my teeth before bed, the corner of my eye caught a glimpse of the pregnancy test sticking out of the trash can. I cranked my head to the side to see, quickly realizing there were two very obvious lines. TWO!

That cannot mean what I think it means...I'm pregnant!

I'm *what*... I dropped to the ground.

"Ryan!" I screamed to my husband from the cold floor of my bathroom. He came rushing in as if the house was on fire.

Have you ever fantasized about how you would announce your pregnancy to your significant other? You know, they would come home from work and you would have their favourite meal ready on the dining room table. They would sit down and right before taking a bite of the picture-perfect meal would catch a glimpse of your oh-so-cute-I-got-it-off-Etsy T-shirt that says "Eating for Two". It would take them just a second to ponder it before lifting you in their arms and you dance around the kitchen together celebrating. Or maybe it's Christmas morning and in their stocking is this perfectly wrapped little box. They open it to find your first ultrasound picture, some confetti and a beautifully hand-written card that announces "Santa's Bringing Us a Baby".

Though I had thought of a zillion creative ways I would reveal our pregnancy to my husband, the thought of actually being pregnant was like the detonation of Tsar Bomba in my head. You can't just conceal such an explosion for the time it takes Etsy to deliver a t-shirt in the mail. I blurted out "WE'RE PREGNANT" faster than I even comprehended what was going on. There was absolutely no space in my mind for containment. And for any of you who were able to pull off a cute announcement to your significant other, I bow down to you.

But back to my pregnancy story.

"We need to go get another test," I tell Ryan.

Although it was the middle of the night, we drove to Shoppers Drug Mart and I ended up buying five different pregnancy tests. Five. And those things aren't cheap. Oh, and a flat of water, because you need to produce a whole lot of pee to take five pregnancy tests in a row. Shout out to Shoppers for being open until midnight. You never know when you will need them for something and on this particular day, *I needed them!* As we drove home, I was slamming back that water as if I just ate a ghost pepper and somehow I found it in me to pee on every single one of those little gadgets as soon as we got in the front door. And, yes, there were those two lines again, a plus sign appeared on the next test, "PREGNANT" screamed at me on the third and fourth, and the last one told me I was four weeks along.

Without a second thought, Ryan starts texting our friends and family the news. I tell Ryan that it's early to announce a pregnancy at four weeks and that most people keep it hush-hush until they make it through that very fragile first trimester.

"Are you really going to be able to keep this a secret for that long?" he asked.

I sat back and thought how far away 12 weeks was and I questioned how anyone can hold in such momentous news for that long. It seemed like a lifetime in itself. How do I go to all my dinner dates, refuse my favourite glass of full-bodied red wine, and think I will be able to hold my secret in? For one thing, I never refuse a glass of wine and, for another, I am the world's worst liar. Even more, I had a trip to New York planned with my best friends and we were leaving in just a few days. How would I keep my lips sealed then? Impossible.

So Ryan and I decided we would tell a handful of our closest friends and family. Only four weeks pregnant and the word was out. And that was that. Our lives were forever changed.

Unfortunately, I cannot end this story with the birth of my beautiful baby. It was during that trip to New York when we were strolling through Central Park I felt a gush. A very big gush. I casually excused myself to the nearest restroom to find myself covered in blood. I ended up going to the Emergency Room to learn, though my baby still had a heartbeat at that time, it was struggling to survive alongside a growing subchorionic hematoma. In not-so-fancy terms, there was a bleed in my uterus. Though I believed that my little nugget was a fighter, I also knew how delicate it was, merely weeks old, and, in the end, it could not endure that growing bleed.

For a few weeks after I returned home from New York, we had follow-up blood work and ultrasounds and there was a point where my husband, my Obstetrician, and I all agreed that we were in the clear. My bleeding had subsided and my baby was growing just as it should, right on track.

We did not find out we lost our baby until our 12 week ultrasound. You feel for the painstaking job of the Ultrasound Tech in these situations. As we excitedly asked question after question about how our baby was doing, she listened attentively while knowing full well that our baby's heart no longer had a beat. As soon as she mentioned she needed to speak to the Radiologist before she could show us anything from the ultrasound, I knew something was wrong.

After we got the news, I drove home alone and completely numb. My husband — bless his heart — went straight to his shift at the Fire Hall. At the time, we didn't know any better. We didn't realize that going to work was probably not his priority after getting such news. But, as I said, we weren't expecting this outcome as we thought we had overcome the bleed. Being the man that he is, he had the responsibility to go to work, so off he went. I, on the other hand, went home by myself completely lost.

The next day we were given the option to take medication to help the pregnancy come to an end, have surgery, or let things happen naturally. I remember feeling so much hatred toward my body. How my body could let me down in the worst possible way. What frustrated me more than anything was I still felt the regular symptoms of pregnancy even after learning my baby hadn't survived. My boobs ached, I was extra tired, nauseous... or was I? Maybe I dreamt those symptoms up in my head, I thought. I was embarrassed to think I did not know my baby was no longer alive inside me. How could my body continue to give me all the signs that I was nourishing this growing baby when really I wasn't?

Before I needed to go in for surgery or take a pill my body ended up taking care of things naturally. I think it heard the cries from my brain telling it to let go of our baby, and my body finally obliged.

I can honestly say after I had let go of that pregnancy and my baby and life was "back to normal", I never felt so alone. Which is confusing to admit when you have one of the most supportive husbands on the planet right there alongside you. I also had an incredibly supportive sister, mom, extended family, and friends, yet I felt very much isolated from everyone. None of those people holding my hand, hugging me, and standing by me as I grieved were responsible to grow this baby except for me. None of them were this baby's protector and nurturer, except me. That was all on *me*. How could anyone understand how I was feeling?

I went through some therapy, a couple of months of tears, and triggers at the grocery store when I would pass by someone sporting a baby bump. Those baby bumps were everywhere it seemed, it was like it was the trend of the season. My most important job as a mother was to protect my baby and all I kept telling myself was that I failed. Not only did I fail my baby, but I failed myself and I failed my husband. I also felt as though I had failed my in-laws and my parents. I had taken the gift of a grandchild from them. The guilt made its way into my nightmares and fears of what my future fertility journey would look like.

Luckily, there was a time in which I experienced a turning point in my grief. It was about three months after the miscarriage when my therapist suggested I attend A Walk to Remember, which is an event organized by the Early Pregnancy Loss Clinic in my community where you send in your story and they would dedicate a memorial to the baby you lost. I mentioned it to my mom and my sister and without even a second of contemplation, they asked if they could attend with me.

Well let's just say we cried from the second we showed up until the second we left that day. We cried hard. We cried ugly. And my sister and mom who hadn't gone through what I went through, cried just as hard as I did. They cried for me, they cried for Ryan, and they cried for our loss. I realized right then and there I really wasn't alone. Those people whom my husband and I decided to announce our pregnancy to, a mere four weeks in, were a part of our journey every step of the way. I realized that those people cared so much for us that it was a loss to them as well. Every person that knew about our pregnancy, and our subsequent miscarriage, ended up being the best support system I could have asked for. They loved me so much they let me grieve however that meant, for as long as I needed, and they were right alongside grieving with me. They were there for me so much more than I could comprehend at the time.

You may be wondering why I didn't attend A Walk to Remember with my husband. At that point in our journey, we began to learn that we were grieving very differently. What I needed for healing was unlike what he needed and so we did our absolute best to support each other, but we never forced a certain way onto one another. There were times when Ryan needed the company of our friends as support around him, but it wasn't always something I could handle early on in the loss. So he would go out and I would stay home to snuggle my dog and we both understood each other's actions were for our own healing. We also had our time together to grieve, talk, and embrace each other, but some of our therapy methods were separate and that worked for us.

For those of you who read this story and it resonates with you, maybe you too have experienced a miscarriage, maybe you have experienced infertility, a stillborn, or any other struggle whatsoever, my heart aches for all of you. For those of you who cannot relate, not to be the bearer of bad news, but life is full of tribulations. We will all feel pain and unbearable sadness one day as we navigate through life, but we can also trust that we will be able to find a blessing or two within our journeys. We all have stories that change who we are — at the core of our being — but that doesn't give us a free pass on the sympathy train. I dare you to look for the positive in the sea of dark, the rainbow within the storm.

As I look back it seems unfathomable to think Ryan and I would have gone through our miscarriage without the support of our closest friends and family. It didn't take 12 weeks for our pregnancy to become real to us. It was real from that first positive pregnancy test. But it was during A Walk to Remember that I looked over at my mom and sister and truly felt grateful for them and all the blessings I have in my life every day.

I vowed, then, to always be grateful for the life that I live, and the people that surround me and are always there to support my family. That adjustment in my perspective was life-changing. Having a positive outlook is a skill that has strengthened my mental health and has helped me become a better version of myself and, in turn, a better mother. I urge you to do the same.

Blessings are considered something beneficial for which one is grateful. That means a blessing can be *anything at all*. Is the stranger that helped you cross the street as you struggled to scoop up your screaming baby, your groceries, and everything else a packhorse needs to carry a blessing? Is your health a blessing? What about your baby's health? Is it a blessing that your neighbour mowed your lawn for you because he knew your husband was working night shifts all week? What about the mail delivery guy who decided to tell you a knock-knock joke when he dropped off your package? Funny or not, it would lighten your day, I am sure of it.

A CHALLENGE FOR YOU

At the end of each day write down three blessings that you have in your life. Maybe it is something that you experienced on that particular day that resonated with you. Are you grateful for your beautiful home, or the phone call you received from your grandma that day? Maybe it's someone in your life that you are grateful for: an amazing partner, a supportive father or a fur-baby that wakes you up every morning by licking your face. Make an effort to do this challenge for 30 days, with the goal that this will become a habit in your life and change your way of thinking. There is much controversy around the time it takes habits to be formed, but we do know that the most important step to creating a habit is *consistency*. So, once you have done this exercise for 30 days, do it for another 30 days and then another.

I use this thought process all the time when I fall off the wagon in my workout routine. I push myself for one month of commitment knowing that the effort will become easier. Soon, I feel as though I *want* to exercise each day because my body and my mind crave it. Even when I do feel like exercising every day, my work isn't done. I have just begun to recognize this healthy habit as an important part of my daily routine and appreciate the benefits it brings to my life. That recognition is what makes continuing to pursue my goal a little easier.

Being grateful and aware of what we have sends a message to our brain telling it to surround our thoughts with the rainbows of life instead of the rain. Write down your three blessings on a sticky note and stick it somewhere you can see them. Post it on your bathroom mirror or the dashboard of your car. Tack it on the bulletin board in your office, tape it to your bedpost, or write an ongoing list on your phone. Put it somewhere that is available to you to see every day during your daily routine. Allow yourself to walk by your list and read them over and over. Here are my three blessings today:

1. The weather was beautiful.
2. I pulled three ginormous beets out of my garden. (I am a mediocre gardener at best, so this is a momentous blessing!)
3. A stranger held the door open for me at the mall.

Was your latte from your local coffee shop on-point or did your favourite song come on the radio right at the time you needed a pick-me-up? If you see it as a blessing, then it's a blessing. It's that simple. Do you know what my three blessings were yesterday? I'll tell you!

1. I have an amazing husband.
2. I slept in while Ryan took Matteo to the park. Halleluiah!

3. We had a family dinner and I spent some quality time with my nieces and nephews.

So, I ask you, can you find your blessings? They are there, I promise you. I must give credit to one of my favourite authors for this exercise. I started doing this after reading Rachel Hollis's book, *Girl, Stop Apologizing*. If you haven't read her work, I highly recommend it. One of her exercises, exactly like I am asking of you, is to practice gratitude daily. She says to write down ten things you are grateful for each day. Her words exactly: *"if you spend your day looking for blessings – here's the magic – you'll find them"*.[16]

Instead of ten, as Rachel requests, I am asking you to just start with identifying three blessings. I am saying three because I'm writing this book for all the new moms out there. This particular audience, as we can all attest to, has limited time because of the overwhelming amount of responsibilities and tasks parenthood fills our life with each day. I don't want you to skim over this exercise because it's just too unbearable to add one more thing to your daily list of chores. Writing down only three would take less than three minutes. Three minutes, ladies! We can fit that in. I'm not even asking you to find three minutes *more* in your day. You can do it at the same time you brush your teeth! While you're brushing those pearly whites before bed tonight, ask yourself, *what are three things that happened today I'm grateful for?* Write it down. That's it. And I know you're all brushing your teeth every day... right? After you create this habit it will be ingrained into that beautiful brain of yours and your mind will transform to seek out the positives in your life each and every day.

Now, there is just one more step to this practice: each morning when you get out of bed, before you check your phone, and before you run into your child's room to meet their needs, recite those three blessings that you wrote down the night before. Start your day off by reminding yourself of what you were grateful for yesterday. **Opening your day to feelings of gratitude sets your intention for the rest of the day** and that's one small – but momentous – practice for a healthy mindset.

5
THE POWER OF A LITTLE FRESH AIR

Getting the Heck Out of your House

GET out and smell the roses. I mean this figuratively — let's appreciate what is often ignored as the analogy suggests — but I also mean this literally. Get out of your house and spend time outdoors. I promise you will feel better. Seriously, it is that simple.

To someone who isn't a new mom, getting out of your house is so very basic. Don't forget your pants, lace up your shoes, and you are good to go. With a new baby in tow, it's not such a simple task. Do you have the baby wipes, bug spray, sunscreen, sun hat, snacks, bottles, binky, teething toys, backup teething toys, wipes for the teething toys, blankets, spit-up cloths, bibs, Kleenex, boogie wipes, hand sanitizer, backup outfit, socks, oh and did I forget the diapers?! Sometimes, as new mothers, we would rather raise the white flag, surrender, and stay inside.

Let's just cozy up in our pajamas and call it a day. Seems much easier, doesn't it? But even though it is *easier,* it isn't *healthier.*

Getting out of the house each day for some fresh air is imperative and that's the hill I'm going to die on. This does not have to mean full elaborate outings to the local museum or a trip to Disneyland. Getting out of your house could be as simple as a walk to your mailbox. For each of you, different outings may make more sense for you and your baby. Outings could include a trip to the grocery store, a mommy-and-me workout class at your local gym, or even splashing around the puddles on your driveway. Heck, maybe for you it means loading your baby into the car and going through the Starbucks drive-thru for a matcha latte.

No, I did not forget about those strict baby schedules we're all slaves to — sticking to nap times, and bath times, and bedtimes — but I know you all have it in you to plan a little bit of 'fresh air time' into your day. Your soul will thank you, I guarantee it.

I live in the North. Edmonton, Alberta, Canada to be exact. If you don't know much about Canada or the Alberta prairies, I'm sure you at least know that it's cold up here. Not cool, cold. Like, freeze your buns off cold. There aren't many cities on the planet colder than us. Our winters are harsh, so I don't want to hear any of you use 'weather' as an excuse to stay inside! Okay, unless there's a tsunami... but I will only give you grace for a tsunami because we don't get those up here and they sound terrifying.

Living in the Great White North entails additional preparation for mothers. To get our little bundles of joy out of the house between October and March means wrapping our babies in full-body snowsuits, thick socks, boots, blankets, gloves, hats, and scarves. We pack all that is needed to keep our babies comfortable in well-below freezing temperatures, on top of cramming everything else an infant needs into our overflowing diaper bags. If we Canadians can do it, you can do it too. As I write this chapter, it is April and we are currently amid a 20 centimeter snowfall. As brutal as it is, Matteo and I bundled ourselves up this morning and made snow angels in our backyard. Well, I made a snow angel as he stood there staring at me as though I had lost my mind. It wasn't very long before we were back inside, but we made it out for some fresh air and *that* is what counts.

Other winter activities for us include time at the library and indoor walking tracks that are stroller-friendly, like our community recreational center. We also visit indoor play places and go swimming in indoor pools. We have playdates at our friends' houses, remembering the importance of having people in your life that are in the same life stage as you with little ones. There are always winter festivals that include fun activities, craft shows, and indoor light shows. Sometimes we go to the local mall just to window shop. Use your imagination!

When Matteo was fresh out of my womb, a friend of mine told me that the more you practice getting out of the house, the easier it will become. She mentioned this to me after I had been late — more than once — to our scheduled plans and she could see how much getting out of the house was stressing me out. It unnerved me to the point that I preferred not to go out at all rather than miss a good chunk of our plans before we had to get back home for naptime. In the beginning, it felt as though every time I made the effort to get out of my house, something always seemed to happen: a last-minute poop explosion, a spur-of-the-moment feed, or I had forgotten the entire diaper bag at my front door. It seemed that no matter how much extra time I anticipated, I always needed more. Nonetheless, I will be the first to admit that she was bang-on with her advice because it *did* get easier. The more I pushed myself out of the house, the more of a routine it became.

I started practicing with plans that weren't on a strict timeline. I would rehearse packing my diaper bag and loading Matteo into the stroller just to walk over to the local convenience store. I didn't sign myself up for that 45-minute stroller-cize class ahead of time because I knew that there was a strong possibility of walking in 40 minutes late. Instead, I would try to make it to the gym by a certain time and, if the stars aligned, then to the class we went. If it didn't work out for us and we were behind on our schedule that day, then I would grab my baby carrier and, with Matteo strapped in, would walk around the indoor track at the gym instead. I also always kept our swimming bag in the trunk of my car so that, if all else failed, we could spend some time wading in the tot pool that was open all day at the same gym. Having a backup plan encouraged me to get out of the house each day because I knew that all of my efforts wouldn't be for nothing if I was late to my original plan.

Some of you may admit that running late is a big stressor in your life, while others may not give an ounce of thought to it. Even if you do not experience the anxiety that many do feel when late, it could mean those around you worry for your safety if you do not show up when you said you would. No feelings toward tardiness are positive ones. Having the skill to get out of the house on time, without a sense of panic, gives us some control to our chaotic lives. Punctuality is better for our well-being.

A CHALLENGE FOR YOU

When learning how to get out of the house with a baby on time start with setting a goal for yourself. For example, *"I want to get out of the house by 11 am today."* Practice with a plan that doesn't have a specific start time, like a trip to HomeSense or the grocery store. Do this when your calendar is wide open and you have no responsibilities to anyone other than yourself and the schedule of your newborn because, well, that is hard enough. Keep track of how much time it takes for you to pack the diaper bag, change your baby's diaper, put your own pants on (don't forget your pants!), probably change another diaper, and get out of the house. Continue to practice it again and again until you recognize, roughly, the amount of time it takes for you to get out of the house with a baby. Now, add an extra 15 minutes to your estimated time and use *that* as your baseline for any future plans.

There has never been a time which I regretted adding 15 minutes to my plans. In fact, if I was ever early to my destination, I would make sure to treat myself to a little self-care with that extra time. If Matteo was content in his car seat, I would sip on my coffee, make a phone call to a friend, or even just recline in my seat and enjoy a moment or two of silence. On really lucky days I would read a few pages of a book; I always try to leave some good reading material packed in my diaper bag in case, by some off chance, I find some downtime. This is a habit that I learned from my mom who spent about a quarter of a century in her minivan driving her four children to multiple practices, sporting events, and birthday parties on any given day.

If Matteo just wasn't having it that day, I would take him for a stroll around the block, have some cuddle time, or breastfeed before our scheduled plans. Creating that extra time in my day gave me a little sense of freedom and a lot more control over the busyness of my life. I carried this skill forward when I was ready to return to work after my maternity leave. Before returning, I made an intention to learn how long my morning routine needed to be to get myself ready and get Matteo ready for the day. With a solid understanding of my needs and an extra 15 minutes for comfort, I never leave the house in a flurry before a busy workday.

Switching gears now this is, yet again, another strategy that may seem impossible due to the global pandemic we have recently been faced with. It may be a long time before we witness our outings, in-person group activities, and, well, society as a whole operate as it had pre-COVID. Technology and virtual meetings may continue to be the first choice for socialization, making us believe that "getting out" is now an unattainable task — especially since many have experienced city-wide lockdowns. Well, Mamas, I understand! I was on maternity leave during our first lockdown and I will tell you maternity leave on a good day can feel extremely isolating. So, locking down the entire city that I was living in did not do anything to help me to get out of my house and into the community that I craved to be part of.

Before COVID-19 I spent so much of my time at our local rec centre in order to get out of my house each day when, all of a sudden, it was taken away. I needed to get creative. Luckily, it was summer so Matteo and I had picnics in our backyard, storytime on our balcony, and some days we would simply open our windows as wide as we could to blow bubbles out the screen. Let's not use

COVID-19 as an excuse to give up on our mental health. Similar to our need for supports around us as we learned in chapter 3, this is one more example that proves mental health strategies should be more of a priority for us than ever before. Though our lockdown plans were not ideal, we did whatever we could to feel fresh air through our hair and sunlight on our cheeks.

I want to end this chapter with a story about a good friend of mine. She was someone who delivered her son only a few weeks after I had Matteo, so I daydreamed about the maternity leave we would take together; play dates and park dates, swimming lessons with our boys... those two were going to be best friends. Soon, one month went by, and then another, and another, and I couldn't seem to make plans that she would stick to. No matter what I suggested we do, she refused to join or would cancel on me last minute.

Finally, about six months later, she called me up and said that she and her son would be joining the mom and baby workout session at our local gym that Matteo and I attend. I was ecstatic and we ended up having the best time together. From that day forward, she had plans to get out of her house every single day. She would go swimming with her son, walk the track at the gym or outside around the walking path in our community, and even joined a stroller-cize class three times a week. I honestly couldn't keep up!

One day over a cup of coffee, she opened up to me about her struggle with postpartum depression and explained why, for the first six months after having her son, she isolated herself. Between the overwhelming feeling of learning how to become a mom, the guilt she felt about her Caesarean section, and the NICU admission her son had at a mere two days old, she was overwhelmed so she hid from the world. The day that she called to join Matteo and me on our daily outing, she described it as an internal voice of reason telling her to persevere. When she finally forced herself out of her house, her life changed drastically.

Staying inside and away from others, just as my friend did, is considered a coping mechanism of our minds, though we may not even be cognizant of this. When we are feeling anxious or depressed, our minds tell our bodies that we are safest within our "box" and anything outside of these abstract boundaries of safety is full of the unknown. So, yes, the familiarity of our box is comforting. Being outside of our homes may mean that we are outside of our comfort zone — especially since we feel the need to protect our new baby from all the bad in the world — making this exposure feel overwhelming. What's worse is the more we give in to this coping mechanism and only stay within these boundaries, the smaller our box becomes. You may start avoiding certain places (such as big, crowded malls or grocery stores) but this has the potential to lead to more places that become off-limits. Soon, something as simple as a visit to a friend's house may be too much for you. The problem with avoidance is it never gives you the chance to challenge your thoughts. You may think, *"the library is so dirty and crowded with people, my baby will get sick"*, but what if you challenge those thoughts, go to the library and return home without your baby getting sick. It is only then you have proven the fallacy within your mind. We have to interrupt those thoughts of fearfulness that may cause untruths to become our reality. If you never defy your feelings, then that's the existence you have created and the truth that you live in.

I consider that girlfriend of mine an inspiration to all new moms out there. Her determination to feel better for herself and her son allowed her to finally enjoy her transition into motherhood. She is one of the happiest, most energetic people

I know and truly the best mother she can be to her son. And, if you don't want to listen to me about the importance of getting out of your house, I hope her story will teach you the power of a little fresh air.

IF MENTALLY WE AS MOMS AREN'T RIGHT, IT REFLECTS IN EVERYONE AROUND US

-Taylor F.

Mom to Stella and Baby #2 on the way

6
"MOMS ARE SELFISH," SAID NO ONE EVER

Selflessness Begins with Selfishness

I feel the need to start this chapter off with a warning: you are going to hate it.

You are going to hate this chapter because it's not about your baby, it's about *you*. You are going to have to get selfish and it's probably going to be one of the most difficult requests anyone could ask of any new mom, putting *you* on your priority list! If you stop to think of all the women that you know in your life, can you think of anyone that puts herself before others? As sad as it is to admit, I can't.

I know you're killin' it as a mom and I'm sure you're also rockin' it as a wife, a sister, a daughter, and a friend, but, I ask you, how good are you at taking care of yourself? Now, more than ever, this is by far the most important part of your game. Without healthy moms, how are we going to raise healthy babies in healthy households?

Matteo is a wonderful baby but he definitely won't win an award for being an astounding sleeper any time soon. Since his birth, there has been a total of... let me think... one, *just one*, night that he slept for eight hours straight. Instead of me also getting a decent night's rest that *one* night, I was pacing his nursery wondering if he was alright, but that's a story for another day.

To paint you a picture of who I am, I thrive off of ten hours of sleep a night. I would take 12 if I could get it, but I will settle for ten. Not eight like a normal human, not nine, but ten full hours of sleep. So, you can imagine the toll a new baby took on me when my new normal became one-quarter of the sleep I need to survive. My husband is very much aware of this and will caution me when he can see my wholesome self getting chipped away like a woodpecker chiseling out the side of a cedar. "It's better for everyone if you take a nap now, Kristy," is his most polite way of saying I'm acting like a demon.

There was one particular time when Matteo was about eight months old, and the lack of sleep had officially caught up to me. I felt as though I had done really well treading water for so long, but I was too exhausted to stay afloat. Slowly, I was drowning in sleep deprivation and this did not go unnoticed in my household.

My husband continually offered to wake up with Matteo during the nights so that I could catch up on my sleep. He suggested he be responsible for Matteo's nighttime feeds and would warm up the pumped milk in the freezer, so this wouldn't be a problem whatsoever, but every night he would ask and every night I would refuse.

"I will wake up either way when I hear him."

"My boobs will explode if I don't feed him, I'd rather just do it."

Excuse after excuse; I always thought I could just endure through. I honestly knew full well that if I got a little more rest I would feel so much better, but that wasn't my priority. I was a new mother who was ready to take on motherhood like a bull charging a red flag. Nothing was going to get in my way to be the most dedicated mother to my son. I most definitely wasn't worried about me and my sleep, or lack thereof; I was focused on one thing and one thing only — to take care of my baby!

Well, one day as Matteo and I were headed downstairs for breakfast, my husband took Matteo out of my arms and told me to get ready for the spa because that is where I would be all day, and there was no refusing it. He skootched me out of the house as he and Matteo waved me good-bye.

The guilt when I left for the spa was undeniable. It hurt my heart. I felt so selfish. Why did my husband think I needed time away from my family? Did he think I was incapable of handling motherhood? Did I really deserve a day of pampering? I mean, every mom is doing what I am doing! It's what I signed up for and now my husband thinks I'm struggling. Of course, these thoughts made me internalize feeling of complete parent failure.

Before I continue with this story, I must tell you that I contemplated sharing it with the world. A day at the spa seems extravagant and a little over-the-top for me, and it paints a picture of a luxurious life that isn't exactly relatable. But I have to be honest, this experience and what I learned that day was life-changing and, though I don't spend days on end at the spa, it was a gift my husband gave me that he felt was necessary at that point in our journey. That day, Ryan knew something at the time that I did not: **I could not be the best mother to my son when I had completely cut myself off of any self-love.**

Needless to say, as soon as I walked into the spa and put on a fluffy white robe and some spa slippers, I felt as though I had walked through the gates of heaven. Not only did I have the most relaxing day, but I slept. I slept so hard. I slept during my massage, I slept in the sauna, and the meditation room. I am pretty sure I even fell asleep in the shower. By the end of the day, I was so rejuvenated, I felt like my old self again. The person I hadn't seen for eight months. *Hey, Kristy, it's been a minute, nice to have you back!*

After the spa, the second I walked in my front door I swept Matteo into my arms while beaming with energy. I have no doubt Matteo could feel the change in my demeanour too. It didn't take long after my self-care to witness the devoted, enthusiastic mom I am when I feel like my healthy self. When I am rested, I am eager to sit on the floor right alongside Matteo in his playroom instead of lying like a log on the couch watching him from afar. I am interactive and respond to his coos and babbles instead of dazing into dreamland as he tries desperately to communicate with me. I am keen, affectionate, patient, and loving. My normal healthy self brings out the *quality* time for my family.

Since then, I have shifted my mentality, slightly, and have added myself to my priority list. It doesn't need to be an elaborate day at the spa to get yourself to where you need to be (or maybe it does, no judgement!). Maybe it's ten minutes of meditation in the mornings or an episode of your favourite TV show (I will list some other common self-care options below). I now nap when Matteo is napping on the days that I feel tired, and without any guilt, may I add! Even if those dang dirty dishes from breakfast are screaming at me for a good scrub or my dinner menu needs to be a little less extravagant today than the Rigatoni Lamb Ragu that I made the day before (just kidding, my fanciest meal is veggie tacos), there is still no guilt. Trust me when I tell you that there is no meal out there worth having to deal with the wrath of a sleep-deprived Kristy. I know my husband will second that.

A fancy dinner isn't the only chore that is sometimes put on the backburner for the sake of taking care of me. Those weeds in my garden, the extra presentation I'm creating for work, the dog walks, the emails I need to check, they can all take a back seat for the time it takes for a little self-care. Some nights, I will turn on 90 Day Fiancé and enjoy every single minute of it even though my floors are a mess and I didn't clean up the playroom. When I take a little bit of time to revive myself, I know I will get to those floors and that overflowing playroom without skipping a beat. If you think that's selfish, then I encourage you to consider that when you give time to yourself, you are also giving more to your child. To be a better you and a better role model for those munchkins looking up to us each day. (The role model in me doesn't allow Matteo to witness me tranced into 90 Day Fiancé, by the way).

Though we may not know each other personally, I would bet that you are a mom that loves your baby with all your heart, but all that energy you give to your baby takes away from the care you give yourself. I hope you will come back to this chapter to remind yourself over and over *that it's okay to take care of yourself* too. It's more than okay, I absolutely demand it! It's normal to feel as though there aren't enough hours in a day with a new baby to love yourself. I've been there. My fellow new moms have been there too. I'm here to tell you that if you allow yourself just a little bit of that love, you will be pleasantly surprised by how much better you will feel emotionally, mentally, physically, and spiritually. Let's create a new normal that allows us to take care of ourselves with as much love as we give to our babies.

HEALTHY SELF-CARE SUGGESTIONS

- Yoga
- Meditation
- Exercise
- Journaling
- Reading
- Social groups or sports teams
- Quality time with pets

But don't stop there! Only you know what gives you the respite to fill your tank back up. If you don't know, start trying new things; you may be surprised by what you learn about yourself or the skills you could gain that make you feel as though you are relaxing, resting, and taking time for yourself and nobody else. I never journaled until after I had Matteo but started because the release was something I felt I needed, and it is now one of my daily practices. I know moms that spend some time knitting sweaters, sewing, painting, playing video games, board games, carpentry, baking, taking online classes, gardening, and even karaoke.

Understand, too, that self-care can be small things. Making big changes to your routine can be overwhelming, so sticking to those plans will be that much harder. Start with small goals for self-care — listening to music for example — so that it's easy to include it into the busyness of your life.[17]

Exercise is another self-care strategy that works great for me; I enjoy anything and everything that will get my heart rate pumping and a little sweat pouring off my brow. At this stage in my life, to keep things fresh, I don't commit to one exercise in particular, though I know many moms who are avid runners, hikers, or yogis. Some days, it's important for me to go for a walk while I read a book. Other days I'm eager to sprint intervals. On another day, you may see me in the gym lifting weights or outdoors playing a sport with my husband and friends. Spikeball, anyone? The idea is all the same: get my energy levels up, burn off some steam, and clear my head. Getting your body moving and blood flowing is a physical way to a healthier well-being. It's proven that exercise releases naturally-occurring stress-fighting hormones and endorphins that are linked to feelings of happiness and mood stability. Releasing these during exercise increases good feelings, while lower levels in our bodies can be related to feelings of depression and anxiety.

A CHALLENGE FOR YOU

Brainstorm ideas on how you can make time in your schedule for a little self-care. Is there someone you can utilize to babysit so that it's possible to take action on some "me-time"? Maybe your mother-in-law can come over once a week so that you can take a bubble bath. If you think she will roll her eyes at you for suggesting this, well then just tell her you'll be upstairs cleaning the bathroom. Maybe instead of a coffee date with your girlfriend and her baby, you could take both babies one day and she can take them the next so that you have some baby-free time. I know certain moms that decided to sleep-train to guarantee extra hours of shut-eye and fewer wakeups in the night to get the rest she needs. Is hiring a cleaning or meal prep service an option? I'll talk more about prioritizing in chapter 12.

IF YOU ARE STILL NOT CONVINCED OUR BABIES BENEFIT FROM OUR SELF-CARE...

Having worked on a maternity unit, more times than I can remember, new mothers would call me into their room and their baby would be crying uncontrollably. They would be holding their little nugget in their arms as tight as they could, rocking them from side to side desperate for them to stop crying.

"Nurse, I don't know what to do. My baby won't stop crying! Help me," they would plead. These new moms were so distraught and overwhelmed with the life they were now responsible for.

More often than not, we nurses would scoop those babies up in our arms and the baby would settle down instantaneously. Is it because we maternity nurses have been given baby whisperer powers from God himself? Maybe. Or maybe there could be another explanation: **babies feel our emotions.**

Every time I was called into a room and the baby would not settle after being fed, changed, and cuddled, it was because the mother was overwhelmed and the baby could feel it. Those maternity nurses that can settle a baby like nobody's business aren't carrying feelings of sleep deprivation, pain, angst, and nervousness of not knowing how to care for their little ones and is why it's possible for them to so easily settle a crying newborn.

Imagine being a brand-new baby fresh out of the womb. You've lost all you have known inside those walls of the uterus and are now in an unfamiliar, overstimulating environment. You want — *you need* — to be protected by your mama. That's all a newborn is trying to learn: *"How do I survive in this big scary world?"* You rely entirely on cues from your mom about the world around you and you are learning about your new environment simply by how your mom is reacting to it. Instinctually, when she is stressed, you associate that with a threat. When a calm human rescues you from the situation, you feel the protection you have been looking for. You feel safe again.

Not only are our babies cognizant of our stress, but they also have physiological changes of their own in reaction to our stress, described as *emotional contagion*. Just like an infectious yawn, you react to something someone else is experiencing. We experience this phenomenon all the time, even when we are not aware of it. Imagine having a conversation with a friend who is complaining the entire time about their job. You are likely to feel more negative than before. Same story with aggression. Feeling aggression from someone else can make you more aggressive; that's usually why a fight breaks out, right?

ANOTHER CHALLENGE FOR YOU

During your next interaction, be cognizant of the emotions that the other person is portraying. Reflect on how you reacted to their emotion during the encounter and then take the time to reflect on how you feel after.

Let's bring some science into this! A study was performed by attaching heart monitor sensors to mothers and their one-year-old babies to record baseline readings of their heart rhythms. After separating the mothers from their infants, the mothers were exposed to a stressful situation. In this instance, they were asked to give a five-minute speech in which they were then given unfavourable reactions from the audience. Most of us can agree that public speaking and public scrutiny are right up there among the most stressful experiences. It's not surprising that those mothers confirmed they felt stressed after such an event and had an increase in their heart rate to prove it. What is surprising, however, was the increase in baby's heart rate after being reunited with their mother; their reaction occurred within mere minutes. Even more, it was found that the higher the stress response in mom, the higher in baby compared to their baseline measurements. This association of reaction in the baby became stronger over time as if it had learned the response from the mother. To further conclude these findings, some mothers, after getting baseline measurements and then being separated from their babies were not exposed to an event that would cause an increase in stress levels. This was confirmed through another measurement, showing no significant change to their heart rate, and in turn, no change to their baby's heart rate.[18]

This chapter is dedicated to all the moms out there who wholeheartedly believe that taking care of ourselves is a selfish act (you know who you are!). Those of you that believe that powering through sleep deprivation, the constant worry, the sore nipples, or the healing C-section scar are what make you the best mom you can be. This is where you are wrong. This is where things need to change. **You are the best mom to your baby when you are the best version of yourself**. And the bottom line is if you aren't going to take care of yourself for you, then do it for them.

7
BEING PRESENT

Preparing for Life while Demolishing Expectations

WHEN I was pregnant, I believed I would deliver before my due date. Spoiler alert: I was well overdue when I had Matteo. I planned to birth my baby without any pain medication on deck. Spoiler alert: I got an epidural. Finally, I knew with every fibre of my being I would deliver vaginally. Spoiler alert: that didn't happen either. I delivered Matteo by Caesarean section. I hope you are getting what I am laying down here. Nothing about this experience happened the way I had planned.

Our pregnancies and our birthing journeys are some of the first moments of motherhood where we are slapped in the face with a loss of control. So much in our lives before this we do have control over. We decide what neighbourhood we live in, what University we attend, which career we will pursue, the cars we drive, if we want to be vegetarian or meat-atarian, who we will marry, or if we even want to get married! Even more, the older we get and the more established we become, it seems the harder it is for us to come to terms with giving up control when our babies come along. Statistics tell us that the average age of entering motherhood is on the rise; meaning even more of us have really hammered down our routine before having it thrown upside down by our children. And, yes, I am one of those statistics because I didn't start a family until I entered into my 30s.

Learning to appreciate the unknowns of pregnancy, labour, and delivery, we begin to understand a little better that the universe is preparing us for all things that will be out of our hands once those little Martians emerge from our bodies and take over our lives (in all good ways, of course). But for whatever reason, as I lost control of my body during my pregnancy and fell victim to an 80-pound weight gain — yikes! — it still didn't occur to me how much was out of my control. And, yet again, I was naïve to the loss of control when I was told after 23 hours of labour that it was time to have major surgery to safely birth my baby. At that time, I didn't comprehend it either. I was surprised by so many things along the way, but it wasn't until I locked eyes with my new baby, overwhelmed with the new responsibility that I began to feel that loss of control brought about by motherhood.

When Matteo was about 48 hours old, a good friend of mine came by for a visit. Nonchalantly she asked me if I was planning on practicing baby-led weaning with Matteo.

Excuse me?

Baby-led weaning?

Like we are talking about introducing solid foods already? This baby is so young I'm still counting his age by hours and you're asking me about solid foods?

Though she didn't mean anything by it, this question took me into a spiral of anxiety. I knew nothing about introducing solids to a baby, which got me thinking of everything else I didn't know. It didn't take long to conclude that I didn't know much about anything when it came to parenting Matteo. Here we are a mere 48 hours in, and I had already fallen off the deep end.

You probably could take a guess at my next step: a Googling rampage. It was as though I needed to learn everything about what was going to happen, and how to avoid all things I didn't want to happen, over the next 18 years of my child's life. I started researching baby-led weaning — the culprit of what started this mess — and from there I came across some baby-friendly recipes, which then took me on an adventure about food allergies in children, which transitioned me into childhood illnesses and then vaccinations... Ahh! You get the picture. The internet is like falling into a toilet spinning 'round and 'round until you're flushed away into the dark tunnel amongst an enormous shit storm. Am I right? To remind you once again, this was day two of motherhood.

The next day, as I nursed my Google hangover, I thought about my journey into motherhood thus far. I had always vowed to enjoy my pregnancy, though I couldn't help to think that my memories of it were murky behind a much clearer picture of very swollen ankles, constant feelings of tiredness, and resentment that I could not live the active lifestyle I was so used to living. I swore I would appreciate my labour and delivery experience, but felt as though the surprises, struggles, and challenges around each corner took me to a place I was not prepared for. I was angry at myself that I couldn't progress further into my labour experience without an epidural, like so many other "strong" women before me. This was something I always thought I had the strength to persevere through. And when the moment came where I was getting rolled on a stretcher into the operating room to have Matteo surgically removed from me, I was focused on this sense of failure; I felt immense shame for my inability to birth my baby.

Now I found myself feeling ill-prepared for all the steps that were to come as I looked at the perfect little nugget cradled in my arms. I was incensed knowing that I should be living in the moment and effortlessly enjoying each day with my baby. Yet, within that same breath, I felt this constant worry for the future. I needed to prepare for Matteo's next milestone, have just the right toys to stimulate him, be on top of his eating, sleeping, and shitting schedule, even though that will all change daily. Though it sounds delightful to just take this parenting journey in stride, one step at a time, one foot before the other, this advice seemed hardly attainable in practical settings.

While preparing the chapter topics for this book, I knew this was a subject I needed to talk about; the importance of taking a breath, knowing where you are at in your journey, and just being present. Yet, I felt as though that was a cop-out to the daily reality of being a mother. Parenting can feel so much more complicated than that, so I needed to dig to the root of what I was struggling with to better share some wisdom with my readers.

One day, I opened up emotionally to a girlfriend of mine. I said to her, "I am not sure how we are supposed to stay mindful and present in this journey of motherhood while simultaneously having all the knowledge and preparation of what the future holds because when trying to focus on one, I get overwhelmed by the other."

Luckily for me, this friend of mine, Rachel, is one of the smartest, most insightful cookies I have ever met and so, even though I had a hard time pinpointing my struggle, she knew exactly what I meant. Her advice hit the nail on the head: "We can prepare, but we need to be adaptable. It is our expectations of the future that give us feelings of anxiety. We want to be in control."

And, you know what? She was right. Let's read those words over one more time, to really carve that into our brains: **we can prepare, but we need to be adaptable.**

As I took the time to think this over, I realized that instead of trying to simply learn about the journey Matteo and I were on, I was trying to control it. When I was preparing for the future, I felt compelled to do things so perfectly that I was trying to rid myself of trials that we will inevitably face. If I could adjust my mindset about my expectations, just as my friend told me, then enjoying the present would not be such a daunting task. This made so much sense to me! The expectations I placed on myself during my pregnancy were not my reality, which is why I was carrying so much resentment. When I was focused on my feelings of failure throughout my labour and delivery experience, it was because it didn't align with the expectations I had created for myself there either. So, I asked, how could I adapt my mindset to rid the expectations I was placing on myself?

That day, my friend taught me about a particular practice I want to share with you. The ideals behind it are central to Buddhism and other Eastern religions, and if you are a yogi you may have learned about it through your yoga practice: *non-attachment*.

The practice of non-attachment is the state in which we overcome our connection to relationships, material objects, and ideas we live by to attain a sharpened and more beneficial outlook of the world. The word itself can be easily misunderstood; non-attached or "detaching" portrays we are turning off our emotions as though we don't care for something, which is not a true interpretation of this practice. Non-attachment teaches us that feelings of sorrow stem from our attachment to something that we have lost, that has changed, or our fear of either of the former. The ideas behind non-attachment support us to diminish our union to the relationships of all things in our lives. It does not require us to give up our goals or desires[19] and it doesn't mean we are not challenged by certain news or situations. **It compels us to be cognizant of when we relate our happiness to the attachment of an idea we want to live up to.** "When we can simply allow life to unfold naturally without being attached to outcomes, beliefs, feelings or opinions, [that is when] we experience true non-attachment."[20]

To understand non-attachment, we need to recognize the fluidity of all things in our world. Absolutely nothing in life is stagnant, nothing is permanent, and simply anticipating that change will occur in all aspects of life will allow us to accept our evolution more easily. Learning to flow with the variability of life enables us to enjoy the experience for what is it without an expectation that it will always be.

If we begin to practice non-attachment, some benefits that are likely to manifest with this practice are:

- More peaceful and less judgemental relationships as you increase your level of self-awareness. When you become more self-aware you may experience your emotions more deeply, but you will not be controlled by them.
- You may feel more resilient toward change because you've gained the understanding that nothing in this world is permanent.
- You may feel a sense of completeness because you no longer desire anything in particular. You can become content in the present moment with who you are, knowing that you are whole in your own way.

- You may feel more love for yourself and others because you're not attaching to beliefs about who you or anyone else *should* be.
- You may become more curious and open to learning new things because you have no fixed expectations when choosing to consider life experiences as your ultimate teacher.
- You may feel more relaxed in life, as you no longer will be controlled by thoughts or feelings, but rather have learned to simply acknowledge it.
- Your mind may feel clearer and you may be able to recognize the truth more easily.
- You'll feel appreciation, love, compassion, and happiness infiltrate your life as you no longer feel the need to chase happiness; chasing happiness can actually create unhappiness.[21]

Make no mistake, non-attachment is a practice that we must consciously bring into our lives. It is not something that we just do. Attachment truly is human nature — think of your bond to your family, your relationships, and even personal belongings — but learning about non-attachment helps us stay in check of what we desire in life.

"Detachment is not that you should own nothing, but that nothing should own you,"
Ali Ibn Abi Talib (Islam)

In the world of motherhood, non-attachment teaches us to release any expected outcomes of our parenting journey. We may relate our feelings of happiness to a specific milestone, an accomplishment, the idea of perfection in our children or in our significant other, or the idea of perfection within ourselves. More often than we may be aware of, we carry an idea of what we want to live up to or what we want to experience as we raise our families. If we expect, desire, or believe in any particular outcome of our journey and it doesn't play out as we imagined, we may feel a sense of grief. The trouble lies within the connection between the outcome and our happiness. In other words, if this happens, then I will be happy. Instead, let's sift out those expectations from our beings so that we can appreciate our journey for what it is every step of the way. Along those same lines, we must learn to separate ourselves from what we experience. That means you may have experienced a failure, but you are not failure. Your physical being is separate from your thoughts, your actions, and your behaviours. Understanding this diminishes the possibility of you being defined by what you experience.

Comprehending the principles behind non-attachment is the first step, but how we can adjust our mindset to begin to practice it? Here are some strategies my friend, Rachel, taught me that I hope will benefit you:

Firstly, let's "get in the zone" by getting into the right mindset. You can do this by learning about relaxation and energy releasing techniques such as deep breathing and meditation that can help reduce stress and anxiety, and don't forget the power exercise can have on our mental health.

Rachel also tells us to, "list your values and ask yourself why." This means we focus on living by our values rather than specific outcomes. In doing so, we open ourselves up to more possibilities and to flexibility on how the relationships, situations, and circumstances we find ourselves in play out, while also living by what is truly important to us. More on this in chapter 9.

The next thing she wants us to do is to focus on the present. If we are attached to desires we are always concentrating on the future, which can lead to feelings of anxiety and dissatisfaction.

We must listen to what we need at each moment in time.

"Be flexible" means not getting caught up in the "hows" of life; how will we get to that outcome we desire? Instead, allow for growth as we learn through each opportunity that will arise as we navigate our journey. This idea is also talked more about in chapter 9.

Next, Rachel believes it's necessary to learn to accept uncertainty. Take out the rigidity of our outlook on life. Though we crave so much certainty (yes, that's the control we think we have!), this causes us to become attached to how things play out in our lives, which further adds to feelings of depression and anxiety when life doesn't go exactly as planned. We must remember that we have survived uncertainty before. She says that "when we stop fearing the unknown, we can start to appreciate possibilities."

Another important practice is to stay curious by viewing life as our greatest teacher. We are constantly faced with opportunities to learn and grow as individuals, so focus on what is it that we can acquire from such experiences.

Lastly, we must learn to practice acceptance. Accept everything (people, things, events) just as they are with no desire to fix anything. Rachel says that "part of the path of non-attachment is practicing patience, trust, and faith in yourself and others."[22]

Studies have uncovered postpartum anxiety and depression are closely related to differences between mothers' expectations and the reality of their experience.[23] Challenging these standards is a crucial part of fostering postpartum resiliency. As we practice these concepts, just as with any other exercise we do in life, we become stronger at it. It's the idea of hoping, planning, and dreaming for the future without expecting the results. I didn't need an epidural until I did! And when the time came, I requested it. I didn't need a c-section until I did, and I thank my lucky stars my baby was born perfect and healthy. Non-attachment is a meaningful and deep concept and something many of us are not accustomed to practicing. I bring this knowledge to you for a greater understanding to gain a healthier mindset when our expectations and the control we feel we are entitled to are affecting our well-being.

HOW MY EXPECTATIONS WERE CHALLENGED

I feel the need to share another significant, but very challenging part of my journey into motherhood. Late into my pregnancy and during the entire first year of Matteo's life, my husband suffered — and continues to suffer — from what we have learned to be post-traumatic stress disorder (PTSD). His suffering was brought on by a decade-long career as a first responder and he was debilitated by anxiety and panic attacks. Here we were, days before bringing a baby into this world and my very strong and capable husband was crumbling in front of me. I witnessed him struggle through sleepless nights, constant chest pain, weight loss and then weight gain, nightmares, anger outbursts, feelings of remorse, fear, anxiety, and depression. On top of all of that, as we were trying to learn what was going on, we found ourselves in meeting after meeting with psychologists and trauma therapists, occupational therapists, psychiatrists, insurance agents, rehabilitation teams, and life coaches all trying to get Ryan back on track to return to work at the fire hall. This was in addition to the stigma of first responder mental health and the skeptics presuming he was falsifying his struggles and merely taking a "vacation" from work. To say this was a difficult year for my family would be an understatement.

As I was trying to navigate my new life as a mother, I had a front row viewing of any wife's nightmare. There were so many times I wish I would wake up, hoping what my husband was experiencing was only a bad dream and not the reality we were living. My husband was truly struggling and, though I would give anything to make him feel better, I couldn't end his suffering. All I could do was learn with him along the way.

I did my best to support Ryan, but I am still trying to diminish my feelings of regret in the pit of my stomach from the first year of Matteo's life. I feel regret for not having done more for Ryan during his attacks, for not being more present when he needed to talk, for reacting the way I had in certain situations we found ourselves in, and for the "what ifs" that could have happened if I had done things differently. I constantly wonder if he would be better recovered by now if I had supported him in another way. I also carry a lot of guilt for not being more aware of his suffering before he hit his rock bottom. I feel as though I should have seen more of the signs. Ryan has never said any of this to me and always praises me for being his greatest support, but these are the expectations I put on myself, and are feelings I continue to work through.

This is one more example of how much of life is truly out of our control. Ryan and I spent our 20s creating a dream-worthy life we wanted to live. We wanted to check off as many life experiences as we could and, more than anything, be properly set up to the best of our ability before having children. We were settled in our careers, living in our dream home, and surrounded by a solid foundation we worked hard for to support our future family before we got pregnant with Matteo. Now, as fresh new parents, the life that we pictured was turned upside down. All that we knew was taken out from under us and we question if Ryan will ever be able to step foot in a fire hall again and continue a career as a firefighter.

A CHALLENGE FOR YOU

Think about a significant part of your journey (it could be anything at all: your fertility journey, your pregnancy, labour or delivery, or any aspect of motherhood you have experienced thus far) that you did not anticipate happening as it did. Maybe you assumed you would feel immediate love and connection toward your newborn the second they were born, but instead they felt more like a stranger to you. Maybe you struggled with breastfeeding, struggled with your new body, or the change of the relationship with your significant other. Expectations are everywhere and along every step of our experiences. Once you pinpoint a significant event, write down all the expectations you had surrounding it. Read it over. The next step: throw that piece of paper in the trash.

Honestly, do it!

Toss it out with the garbage because that is where it belongs.

Recognize those expectations you placed on yourself and then physically throw them away forever. Moving forward if you find yourself dwelling on an unexpected outcome, once again, identify what expectations you created and get rid of them. They don't deserve a place in your life if it is only what you had hoped for — not the outcome — that is making you sad. Let go of that control. Own what you are experiencing as your very unique personal story. Be adaptable. Flex with the twists and bend with the turns. It may not play out exactly how you expect, but that doesn't mean the outcome isn't beautiful.

Now for part two, let's practice gratitude. Once again, just as we learned in chapter 4, identify what you are grateful for within that same situation you identified in the first part of this exercise. What can you identify as a blessing, even though the experience did not play out as you had hoped? I will share my three blessings about my husband experiencing PTSD:

1. I am grateful Ryan is strong enough to speak to me about how he is feeling, that he is willing to do whatever it takes to get healthy for his family and that he told me early enough to make changes because we know other families of first responders that weren't so lucky.
2. No matter what Ryan experiences on any given day, he doesn't miss a beat when it comes to parenting Matteo. He truly is the most involved father to our son I could ever dream of.
3. I am grateful for our support networks (made up of many family, friends, and professionals) that are aiding Ryan immensely in his recovery.

I also asked Ryan to complete this gratitude exercise, and these are his three blessings to his journey:

1. His appreciation for the little things has skyrocketed, such as close relationships and time with Matteo.
2. He has been able to pinpoint what he feels is most important in life, allowing him to realize, and live by, his true values and has less of a focus on materialistic items.
3. He has a heightened sensitivity toward others and is more empathetic. He has learned lifelong skills that will better support his mental health, while also having these skills he will be able to help others experiences something similar, which he has already started to do.

Let's change the expectation that we can control everything within our lives and along our journey because, no matter how hard we try to manifest it, we can't control it all. Once we understand the importance of practicing non-attachment, we will become a little more resilient.

It is impossible to think we can live a life practicing non-attachment to perfection, but don't think that is the end goal. If we desire to accomplish non-attachment, *that desire is something we are attaching to.* Instead, we should attempt to simply build upon this practice as we navigate through life. The objective is to be cognizant of our way of thinking and, in turn, react to situations in a way that will better protect our well-being.

So, let's recap. Preparation: yes. Knowledge and understanding: yes. Adaptability: most definitely. Expectations: no. "Letting go gives us freedom, and freedom is the only condition for happiness. If in our hearts we still cling to anything... we cannot be free."[24]

8
PAUSE

Doing your (Proper) Research

LIVING in an era of technological advancement and innovation, having such accessibility to knowledge is power. Individually we are more educated and well-informed than ever before. Or at least we have the means to be. If we don't know something, we have the ability to find out the answers within mere seconds of asking.

Sometimes I find myself browsing my parents' dusty Encyclopedia collection marveling how we ever got by before the internet; even though it is this exact Encyclopedia collection that got me some decent grades in school not so long ago. (If Encyclopedias aren't something in your lifetime and you don't know what they are, just Google it. But I am sure you already have before you even finished reading this sentence). This online way of life is novel and has snowballed in the last few years, changing our culture faster than we can comprehend.

We are privileged to be experiencing motherhood during

a time in which we can be educated on anything we need to know and as quickly as we need to know it. Not only can we gain health-related information, get reassurance about the health of our babies, or be better prepared before seeking a medical opinion,[25] there are also numerous support groups, blogs, and websites dedicated specifically to our community of mothers. We can connect with mothers from all over the globe. That is extraordinary. Blogs and chat groups are an amazing way to feel connected to others, especially with those who find themselves in similar situations. Breastfeeding support groups, Postpartum Mood Disorder chat lines, developmental stages websites, healthy baby-friendly recipes, and arts and crafts projects for kids at any age are all at the tip of our fingers, one click away.

But there is another side to the coin.

Unfortunately, the time in history that social media and other technological platforms began to rule our way of life correlates directly to the skyrocketing rates of anxiety, depression, and suicide we are witnessing within our society. We have lost control of these platforms and a large portion of its positive features have taken a turn for the worse. We are being inundated with information quicker than we have been able to learn how to decipher fact from fiction. Too many times, we are quickly entrapped within the rabbit hole of the internet. One quick Google search on chickenpox can send you into a whirlwind of information; spinning you so quickly within its wrath it's difficult to get out unscathed. It is the inaccurate blogs, videos, opinions, and "experts" that have erroneous messages to spread that make this tool the double-edged sword that it is. Controversial scandals, a difference of opinion that creates segregation of communities, large-scale soapboxes, internet trolls, cyberbullying, and conspiracy theories are a few ways in which the internet can take a toll on our mental health.

Ironically, it is the same platform that has given us such power that is making us feel powerless.

In a perfect world, it is the tool itself that when we ask it for truth on a particular topic, *the tool* will provide us the verity we are seeking. But our world is far from perfect. Due to the internet's highly accessible format, it has become impossible for medical professionals to effectively monitor all health-related information available online to provide us with the real answers and only the real answers.[26] While numerous websites are developed by reliable sources, such as health-care professionals, government agencies, and credible research institutions, just as many are created that are misleading, misinformed, or have another agenda in mind. Unfortunately, it has become increasingly difficult to differentiate between the two, and trying to decipher fact from fiction is a seemingly daunting task. Even more so, it creates an untrustworthy environment and conveys issues of credibility regarding the sites from which health information is obtained.[27] When it comes to the health of our babies, we all want to find the best and the most credible information on the internet, but how do we get there?

Throughout my Masters of Nursing program, we spent countless hours learning how to find and use credible resources for our research. I can say from my education and my personal experience it is not easy! Researchers suggest that the human brain makes decisions in 50 milliseconds of viewing a webpage; if the website looks inviting, positive feelings will be carried forward to other areas of the page, such as in the quality of its content.[28] Web-designers understand this and they capitalize on it when designing a site.

Finding credible sources is even more difficult in this day-and-age because the amount of information at our fingertips is, well, overwhelming. Doing our research is something that I think we should, living in this era, pride ourselves in. I love that this is part of our culture. I do, however, believe it's extremely important to take responsibility for our research and *educate ourselves on how to educate ourselves.*

To do this, I developed a simple way of looking for credible resources on the internet, particularly when looking for health-related information. I want to offer this strategy to those of you who don't find the internet an easy tool to navigate, to those of you who need some suggestions on how to decipher information, and to those who don't know what resources are trustworthy. Some of you are likely experts in this aspect of life and I am sure many of you have a strategy that gives you the peace-of-mind as you seek out information on the internet. But for those of you who are looking for guidance, I want to share a strategy that I find helpful to search *accurately.* While I am searching and when I am looking for information online, I always take the time to **P.A.U.S.E.**

I ask myself: *What is the* ***P****urpose of this site? What are the* ***A****uthor's credentials? Is the information* ***U****p-to-date? Is the wording* ***S****imple enough for me to understand? When I* ***E****xplore other credible sites, do I find similar information?*

Purpose of the Site

Author's Credentials

Up-to-date information

Simplicity

Explore other sites to cross-check information

1. PURPOSE

Websites are *always* developed with a particular purpose in mind. While someone's sole purpose may be to preach to the world their opinion or to make a profit by selling a particular product, others are meant to present the readers with unbiased, evidence-based information regarding a topic. Look for a well-articulated mission statement and values. For example, the declaration, *"We try not to over-simplify the issues discussed on the website, and if there are disagreements in the medical or popular literature on a topic, we point those out as well"* supports the notion that the content of the site is presented in a way that empowers its users to make health-related decisions, not to offer personal opinions or biased information. So, find out the reason for their presence on the internet. *"To sell you our shit"* is probably not the most reliable of all sites.

Diligently look for health disclaimers on a site, which aids in its credibility, but also helps you further understand the purpose of the site.[29] Disclaimers such as, *"the information is not meant to be a substitute for medical advice. When you have questions about your health, it is always advisable to ask a health care practitioner,"* is an appropriate way to identify the site's purpose for its users as information-seeking, not diagnosing or prescribing.

2. AUTHOR'S CREDENTIALS

The credentials of a writer bear no weight in opening a webpage. That means there are *zero* prerequisites required to develop a website. None whatsoever! Anyone with access to the internet can do it. So, find out who the author is and what their qualifications are for sharing such information. Experts in their field have access to a multitude of research papers, articles, journals, other experts in their field, and spend countless hours learning about particular topics. That's their job. Knowing why this person has enough research behind them to share knowledge should be important to you as the reader. It's helpful when a website addresses authors by full name, while also providing a small write-up of their credentials. Many sites may also provide the author's contact information, with the ability for their readers to contact them with questions related to the reading material.

That said, information doesn't need to be discredited strictly because of the credentials – or lack thereof – of the author. There are many instances in which writers will have experts review their work before publication; this should be noted on the site, so do some digging. Other sites use reference lists to substantiate the content and validate the reliability of the information on their site. Hyperlinks are also a bonus on sites that would allow you to gain quick access to the original source.

3. UP-TO-DATE INFORMATION

In our knowledge-driven world, information is constantly changing. What our mothers were told was the right way to do things when they were new parents has probably flip-flopped back and forth a handful of times before we entered into motherhood. This is the internet's greatest feature in comparison to printed material; information can be updated immediately when needed.

What's important about information currency, though, is the frequency of updates on the site no matter if the original information is old or new.[30] This tells the reader that the information has been reviewed and is still considered best practice. Search for initial dates on the information including initial publication date, dates that the information was reviewed, and dates the information was updated. It is our responsibility to be diligent at checking the currency of information and confirm the site is being maintained before trusting its content.

4. SIMPLICITY

Every website must recognize who the target population is and have some understanding of the groups' characteristics so that the development of the web material is appropriate.[31] Sometimes we as readers can find online health-related text material difficult to read, **but readability shouldn't be mistaken for intelligibility.**[32] It is very possible to find websites that are dedicated to best practices and research that present health information in an uncomplicated matter. This can be done so by providing explanations and diagrams of specific terms and health conditions or offering appropriate links to other sites that may further the understanding of a particular topic. Seek out websites that cater to your reading level. If we always look for the most intellectually sounding sites not only will that hinder our learning but, even worse, there's the potential to misunderstand or misinterpret information.

5. EXPLORE

Lastly, if you have found a relevant site that deserves your time and energy, then it is time to cross-check it with other websites. If the information is best practice, it should be sited on several platforms. If you are unable to find the information on any other credible site, this may raise a red flag.

I offer you the P.A.U.S.E. strategy from my professional perspective. I do, however, have a personal opinion on this topic as well: we as mothers need to trust our own instincts when it comes to raising our babies. No website or blog should tell you otherwise. P.A.U.S.E. reflects on our new world that inundates us with information and makes it difficult for us to determine what we believe reflects our values as parents, and as humans, in all aspects of our lives. But the other side to research that I believe is overlooked too often is following our intuitive abilities and our beliefs. To become in sync with these means we take the time to self-reflect. This may mean some important conversations with your significant other or those around you whom you trust. It may also be daily meditation or journaling. You will not learn about the prevalence of measles, or learn about the medical ingredients in every diaper rash cream to make sure you have picked the right one, but we don't really need to complicate motherhood that much. When we take the time to listen internally, we will learn what's important to us, and that is where we may find answers to some of our questions. Never underestimate the power of your instinct. To learn more about the power of choice, read on to the next chapter.

We may never be as sharp as those geniuses behind the development of the online platforms we use and we most definitely will never outsmart the artificial intelligence and algorithms behind every Google Search we perform, every ad we click on, or every purchase we make online, but we can still find a way to use the internet in the most beneficial way. We can use it to keep us, as mothers, educated, empowered, supported, and mentally healthy. *Happy Scrolling!*

LEARN ABOUT YOURSELF AND MAKE DECISIONS FOR YOU AND YOUR CHILD WITHOUT BEING SWAYED BY ANYBODY ELSE'S OPINION

-Kelly M.

Mom to Levi and Suri

9
IT'S ALL UP TO MAMA

Being Empowered by the Power of Choice

AS I am writing this chapter it is 4:17 in the morning and I just finished breastfeeding my eleven-month-old for the third time tonight.

You may have a few opinions about me, as a mother, for what I just told you. My son is eleven months old and still loves the boob and he *does not* sleep through the night!

You may have thought, “Good on you, Kristy, for continuing to breastfeed your son, though he is just shy of one year old.” Or you may be completely weirded out that I continue to breastfeed a soon-to-be toddler.

Others might have thought, “Oh, Kristy, I feel your pain! I, too, am up every three hours because my eleven-month-old doesn't sleep through the night,” and some may be rolling their eyes at me for not sleep training him months ago.

Here, I present to you, ladies and gentlemen, with *the power of choice*.

It is up to *me* to endure through and continue to breastfeed, knowing full well Matteo is only days away from pointing to my chest and saying, "Boobie time!" I am okay with that even though you may not be. It is up to *me* to choose to get out of my warm, cozy bed every three hours to soothe Matteo back to sleep. It is up to *me* to choose to sleep train my son or not. So, let's get one thing straight here: *you* are in control of how *you* parent.

Unfortunately, it's not always as simple as making a decision and sticking to it because this world is full of distractions. We hear opinions, feel judgement, and are constantly bombarded with different options. In fact, the angst that we feel about sticking with the choices we make is because we are sometimes given *too many* options which can take a toll on our happiness; we will come back to that.

In chapter 7 we talked about feeling prepared while letting go of our expectations of the future, so now let's discuss how we get to that point where we feel prepared. As new mothers, how are we supposed to make those really tough decisions for our little ones? You know, those decisions that keep us up at night, fill our minds with stress, and worry us silly as we try to determine what the right thing for our family is. Let's break down the process of decision-making into some easy-to-follow steps. This approach is known as our motherhood decision tree or, our MDT for short. You will see why in just a moment.

STEP 1:

First and foremost, we need to know our **end goal**. We are starting at the end here, Mamas. Yes, it's 4:30 in the morning and, yes, I am a little sleep-deprived. But, no, I'm not talking gibberish.

We are starting backward. When we have a decision that we are struggling to make, we can always wrap it full circle back to the reason we have to decide in the first place. This is the top of our decision tree. This represents the tallest, most lush branches of our tree that catch our eye and it is the most significant aspect to stay focused on. Essentially, our end goal is to meet the needs of our children. So, in the first step of this practice, understand exactly what it is you are looking to accomplish, even when the opinions of others may confuse your thought process. You must filter through all of those distractions and focus on the absolute necessity that is causing you to make a decision in the first place. It is especially easy to get distracted by others as we navigate motherhood for the first time (maybe a little less confident and a little less resilient than we normally are), but if we can stay focused on the end goal, we may be able to identify what, or who, is influencing us.

STEP 2:

After we have pinpointed our end goal, it is time to **identify our values**. We no longer live in a world where pure survival is enough to make you content with your decisions, hence, why there is a need for this chapter. We don't just spear an animal in the forest for dinner because we have to feed our family. Now more than ever before, accessibility in all aspects of our lives is unprecedented and adds a level of disorder to our mere existence. Decisions can be difficult because our values are important to us and we try to live a life that is a reflection of who we are and what we stand for.

So, what exactly is a value?

The definition of a value is, "one's judgement of what is important in life,"[33] and we determine these often through our life experiences.[34] Growing up in a large family, with 17 people over at your house every Sunday for dinner may have influenced how you were raised. You may recognize the importance of this and believe that relationships are a value held dear to you. You may have attended a yoga retreat that changed your life and now thrive spiritually. We can also learn our values through negative life experiences such as the unexpected death of someone very close to us; after such an experience, we may prioritize our health as one of the values we choose to live by. Other examples of values could be adventure, appearance, wealth, kindness, wisdom, creativity, or success, naming only a few here. Write down what is important to you in the choice that you are trying to make. Without having identified values that influence how you want to live your life, there is no difficulty in decision-making and none of this would even matter. Consequently, our values are the heart of our tree. It is the core in which the rest of the decision tree must thrive. Though from an outsider's perspective it isn't easy to point out this aspect of our tree as it stays hidden behind all the branches, we know it's there keeping our tree thriving and healthy.

STEP 3:

Now it's time to do your **research**. Let's take a stroll once again through chapter 8. The importance here is to find reliable information or ask experts for some credible resources. To do this, you can read books, articles, websites dedicated to the topic at hand, but do so without any influence from those around you. You and your partner may find value in researching together, but perhaps it is even more beneficial to do research separately and compare your finding to determine if you came across similar information.

It is then in this next part of your research *after you have learned information for yourself*, you can reach out to others. Seek out people that can provide you with their experiences in the same decision. Remember way back at the beginning of this book I mentioned the importance of surrounding yourself with other mothers? This is one reason it's so important. Ask around. Ask those you respect and who will give you honest answers on how they determined the right decision for their family. Both our independent research and speaking with others are the leaves of our tree. It adds significance and creates a stronger, hardier tree protecting the core of it all: our values.

STEP 4:

It's time we pull it all together. We know our end goal, we have identified our values, we've done our research and asked those who we respect. So, let's **weigh our options**. There are different ways of doing this, but I am not always an enthusiast when it comes to listing out pros versus cons for tough decisions that cause stress or anxiety. Leave those lists for decisions that hold less weight in your world, like when purchasing a new mattress. When identifying pros and cons in decisions that can hold a great deal of importance, sometimes it's dependent on the day what side of the list an item may fall. If that is the case, how do we ever know it's the right decision? When a family member was contemplating a career change, for example, we made list after list of pros versus cons. On one particular day, he identified that a positive aspect of being an entrepreneur was not having a set schedule. But on other days, we recognized that being schedule-free had some downsides, such as needing to be organized and stay motivated. A better way to go about this would be to identify which values coincide with his desire to live by a free schedule. If we went about it this way, we would have recognized he craved independence and flexibility; identifying those values took the confusion out of what side of the list this aspect of entrepreneurship fell on.

With that said, a productive way to weigh your options in your decision-making process is to match them with the values you have identified in Step 2. Take a look at what you have learned through your research and determine how it coincides with your beliefs. Ask yourself: *What have I discovered that reflects on what it is that is important to me and my family?* On the other side, can you point out the ideals that do not match up with who you are to better solidify the principles you want to live by? Uncovering options that align with your values, while dismissing ones that do not truly reflect who you are, will help you to build confidence in your decision-making abilities.

STEP 5:

Finally, we must **make our verdict**. Use that newfound confidence and write out exactly *why* you have decided on *what* you have decided. We need to actually *write it down* so that when others question our decision and we feel distracted once again by outside noise, we will have the strength to defend why it is the best choice for our family. Our value-driven verdict is the stump of our tree. Our decision is strong enough to hold the weight of all the steps above and is solid because we have backing with the work we have done prior.

But wait!

There is one more piece that is incredibly important, which is arguably *the most* essential part; you thought we were done, didn't you? We must, must, must **always be flexible**. This piece is all the things we learned in chapter 7 in a nutshell: we can prepare, but we need to be adaptable, remember? Adaptability is the root of our MDT and its importance is signified because it's our anchorage holding up our tree. Vital to its survival, without it the tree would crumble. It's easy to have blinders on and believe that there is only one way that will work for our family. We can be stubborn buggers sometimes, can't we? But what happens when what you planned for does not work out just as you hoped? This is the point at which our mental health can take a hit. This is where (a) anxiety of the future, (b) depression, (c) mom guilt, or (d) all of the above, sets in. And this is when — and why — we wrap it all the way back to our end goal.

MDT: MOTHERHOOD DECISION TREE

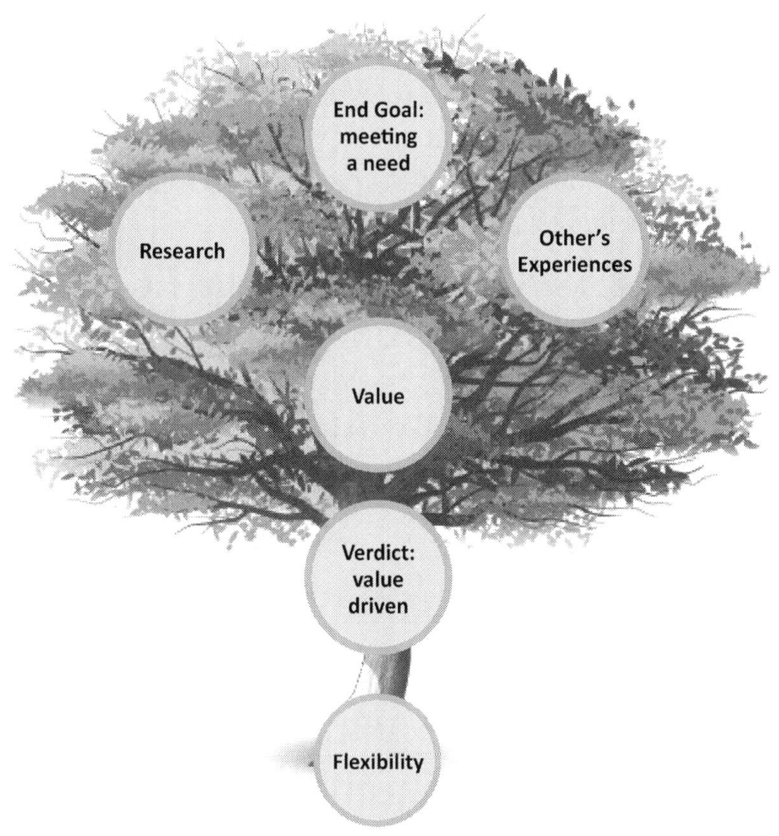

It's time we put this strategy into action and, since we already had some discussion around my decision to breastfeed Matteo, talk about the choices on how to feed our babies. I find this topic extremely important to discuss because many mothers enter into motherhood with a false sense of ability to innately breastfeed. So, if they struggle with it, a lot of angst can arise. On the flip side, I have heard time and time again that mothers who choose to formula feed feel immense judgement from others. This is a frequent topic that can breed anxiety or depression in new moms, so let's explore how you can determine what is going to work best for you and your baby:

STEP 1 END GOAL: Feed your baby.

That's it. As simple as it gets. The most important outcome in this situation and your only end goal. There is nothing that matters more. Your end goal is not to avoid scrutiny from your mother about formula, or to breastfeed simply because that's what you were told is the best thing for your baby. Your end goal: make sure your baby has food in their belly.

STEP 2 VALUES: Some examples of values that hold importance to your family in this example could be:

- *Bonding* between baby and mom. Maybe bonding for all parents or other family members too, that's up to you.
- *Healthy living* and finding the most nutritional option for your little one.
- *Rest.*
- *Financially sound* decisions.

This list could go on and on and nothing is off limits here. It's up to you, though, to recognize what is important for your family in order to live a value-driven life.

STEP 3 RESEARCH: Organizing your research (both independent and then from others' experiences) in a way that coincides with the values identified in Step 2 could look something like the following:

- *Bonding:* You may discover that breastfeeding supports a strong bond between mom and baby, but you question how to create a bonding opportunity for dad. You learn that the opportunity for dad to bond with the baby is possible when feeding with a bottle and is something your significant other mentions as important to them. You also learn, after speaking to a friend, that she found exclusively breastfeeding extremely difficult because even though she had that bond with her baby she could never pass off the responsibility to someone else.
- *Healthy living:* You may learn that breast milk is inclusive of all the nutrition a baby needs for the first six months of life. On the flip side, formula in North American meets high-quality standards.
- *Rest:* Your research may uncover newborns require feeding every two to three hours day and night, so rest isn't exactly on the table here, but you come across a suggestion on a site that mentions splitting up the responsibility between parents allows for longer periods of rest and better respite for both mom and dad. You decide to talk to a mother that breastfed exclusively and she said she absolutely wouldn't do it any other way. This friend actually pointed you to the direction of new research that suggests exclusive breastfeeding offers more rest to mothers because of the hormones that play a role in breastfeeding, while also proving mothers that exclusively breastfeed fall asleep much faster. That means that

even though you are going to be up throughout the night your sleep is more restful!

- *Financially sound:* Breastfeeding is free, which is important for your family and you learn that formula can cost upwards of $3000 each year.

STEP 4 & 5 WEIGHING YOUR OPTIONS TO DETERMINE YOUR VERDICT: Reviewing your values and research you conclude that breastfeeding is important for bonding, checks the boxes of healthy living, and is a financially sound decision. However, it cuts out your husband's desire to play a role in feeding. In conclusion, you determine that breastfeeding and pumping breast milk into bottles for your husband to feed at certain times will support all your values. *Nice work!*

Oh, but we didn't forget about being **flexible,** right? Well, let's just throw a curveball in here. Six weeks after delivering your baby you have horrible pain in your stomach and are diagnosed with Appendicitis. You need emergency surgery, like yesterday, and are heading into the operating room before you even finish saying the word "a-pend-i-ci-tis." (True story ladies! Something very similar happened to my mother after the birth of my sister). During this emergency, your husband picks up some formula because, well, your baby needs to eat and you are not there to feed them, nor have you pumped enough bottles to get through this time. But this was not the decision we made, you say! So, let's circle back to your end goal. Was your baby fed? Yes? Excellent. You got this parenting thing in the bag.

As frustrating as that was, all that work to figure out how you wanted to feed your baby ended up playing out in a way that was not precisely what you wanted.

Welcome to real life.

If we can't roll with the punches, then we are not going to be able to survive motherhood. Anxiety and depression can rear their ugly heads when we are not adaptable. Just like my mom experienced, her plans to feed my sister nothing but breast milk much longer than six weeks all went down the toilet when a life-threatening diagnosis changed those plans for her. As long as we know we are meeting the needs of our baby, we need to stop feeling guilty about the decisions we make. And, side note, how blessed are we to have options such as formula out there for situations such as these?

This is only one extreme example of how life can grab a hold of your expectations and shatter them into a thousand pieces. Sometimes, well most times, it isn't something as severe as a life-altering infection of your organs that plays out in your journey, *but* I do think this example paints us a picture of what can truly be out of our control. And it is situations that are out of our control that can create the hardest times for us to persevere through.

I want to spend just a little more time talking about feeding your baby because, as I mentioned above, a lot of research dedicated to postpartum depression and anxiety is linked to such a choice. Over and over again mothers state that if they did not exclusively breastfeed or ended up giving up breastfeeding altogether, they "failed" at it. Societal messaging tells us that breastfeeding is a maternal instinct. So when mothers are unexpectedly faced with breastfeeding challenges, they believe that they have done something wrong and consider themselves a failure as a mother.[35] The immense power of societal expectations is illustrated throughout literature and is commonly referred to the through mainstream ideas of "good parenting". By accepting and trying to attain this idea of good parenting created by society's standards, studies show that we set ourselves up to more likely experience postpartum depression and anxiety.[36] Let's get one thing straight: exclusive breastfeeding is a tough endeavour. Though it is very possible (for most) to accomplish, it is not merely an instinct in mom and baby that *just happens*. It is a learned skill that can take weeks after delivery — if not months — to even begin to feel comfortable doing.

I work in a hospital that has a world-renowned Baby Friendly Initiative (BFI) designation. We had to work extremely hard to give moms the tools to learn to exclusively breastfeed their baby for the first six months of life and continue to breastfeed beyond that — *if that is the mother's goal.* We have remarkably well- trained staff and resources needed to support breastfeeding moms. The reason for this is many moms who want to breastfeed their baby plan on doing so, but don't have the tools in place to make this a reality. This designation takes years of work to attain and even more work each year to maintain the designation at our facility. This means that the supports our families need to exclusively breastfeed are complex. It is not as simple as delivering a baby that makes you a breastfeeding guru. If it was, then we wouldn't need to work exceptionally hard to keep our designation and a title such as BFI wouldn't even exist. Just remember that you are strong and powerful and you have the capability to work toward any outcome you decide important, but even more importantly, as long as your baby has food in their belly you are doing a great job. Period.

Since we are on a roll, let's discuss one more example we can fit into our MDT approach, with the other topic of conversation in this chapter: sleep training.

STEP 1 END GOAL: Sleep.

That's all, folks. Your baby needs to sleep to grow that brain at lightning speed and sprout like a weed. We don't need to get into the nitty-gritty of teaching our babies discipline or routine here; that could be the distraction, opinions, or judgements we may feel from outside sources. Those can, however, fit into our values section, if it reflects what is important to our family. But it does not belong here. Remember the end goal is the innate need. The most significant and beautiful part of our tree to stay focused on.

STEP 2 VALUES: Here, you may include giving your little nugget the skills to soothe themselves back to sleep. Self-soothing can be represented by values such as:

- *Discipline*
- *Independence*
- *Teaching and learning*

This part of the tree is where all these important values belong. Maybe here you also recognize the importance of:

- *Your rest and recovery* — we didn't forget about you either!
- Maybe you identify that the *refuge and trust* you offer your baby when they need cuddles is the most important value for you and your family.

STEP 3 RESEARCH: Let's organize this with our identified values.

- *Discipline, independence, rest, teaching and learning:* Sleep training offers your family the skills to teach your baby how to soothe themselves back to sleep, without expecting an intervention from mommy or daddy. A friend of yours tells you all about her sleep training journey. She says it was hard for the first three nights, but it was well worth it. Her daughter now sleeps 12 hours straight every night and she feels as though she is the best mom when she is also well-rested. Research supporting sleep training explains the skills your baby learns can aid in better, more restful sleep. It can support you to get a full night's rest, just as your friend mentioned, and has the ability to create independence in your baby.

- *Refuge and trust*: Other research explains that we are social creatures who crave interaction and it is part of our survival. When your baby needs you, you offer them the comfort to know they are being protected, and they will sleep through the night when they are ready. Another friend of yours says that she never trained her son and even though she is still waking up a couple of times a night, she just makes sure she gets to bed early enough to get the rest she needs for the morning. She believes that her choice creates a trusting environment for her son; when he needs her, she is there.

STEP 4 & 5 OPTIONS AND VERDICT: Unfortunately, this decision does not really give you an option for any type of balance. You either are consistent with sleep training for a successful outcome or you decide against it. This is an example where you may need to rank your values to reflect what is most important to you as a family. So, how does all this knowledge you have uncovered align with your family beliefs?

You decide to sleep train because you want to make sure your baby gets all the rest they need and the program you come across offers the skills you feel are most important for you to teach them.

Not done yet, though, because life decided to throw you yet another curveball. After one month of intense sleep training and your baby sleeping through the night, they get a respiratory infection and their stuffiness keeps the entire household up every night for an entire week. Your baby will only settle when cuddled into your chest. But, as you know, the end goal is the sleep that is so important to their growth and development. So, now you are sleeping together in bed, something that you never thought you would do! #Momlife.

The power of choice is well... empowering. The power of choice is also taxing. It is a topic that brings angst to many new moms. Being responsible for another human life, well that's a big undertaking and it comes with *a lot* of decisions to be made. Breastfeeding and sleep training are merely two drops in our parenting bucket. We could do this exercise about baby-led weaning. We could do this in regards to co-sleeping, or room sharing, Montessori programs, or daycare. We could even do this about our labour and delivery plan and I promise you your end goal is to deliver a healthy baby, correct? Your end goal truly is not getting pain medications during your labour or refusing a Caesarean section. Those may be important to you, but if things don't happen as you had hoped and you circle back around to your end goal of delivering a healthy baby, *that is what truly matters*. Focusing on the end goal instead of dwelling on things that may be completely out of your control is what is going to keep you in a healthy mindset.

There is something dually important to talk about here and I am going to sound very contradictory. The truth is most decisions don't require extensive research.[37] Okay, before you throw this book out with the trash because we just spent all that time learning about a strategy I am now saying isn't important, let me explain. I want to tell you that we don't need to dwell or overthink our decisions as mothers. We need to live our lives based on confident decision-making and call it a day. But unfortunately, a challenge for many of us is the validation we feel we need from the people around us. Or, for others, the anxiety we feel when we don't know what is the best decision for our family. That is why I offer you this strategy. I offer this strategy to those who are struggling, those who need some skills to build assurance in their decision-making abilities, and those who are overwhelmed or feel anxious as they try to navigate motherhood. If you know you want to breastfeed your baby until they are old enough to drive, and don't give a rat's ass what anyone has to say about it then, girl, you could come teach me a few things! You hold onto that confidence and run with it.

As mothers, we are under constant scrutiny, judgement, and difference of opinion from pretty much everyone else on the planet at any given moment, which makes you feel a little isolated, doesn't it? I have to point out the glasshouse here ladies; much of the time it is other mothers — such as ourselves — that are the ones doing the judging. Don't we have enough to do in our own homes? Why worry about what's going on in someone else's? Many times we mean well, but I just want to call attention to one small fact here: we are all adults with the ability to process information and make decisions. So don't think you can do it better than another mom. If she parents differently than you, it's probably because her family values are different than yours. Does that make her wrong? More often than not, it doesn't. You may be the Queen of Manners and will have the most polite children on the planet, but she is the best Arts and Crafts Instructor and her daughter is going to be the next Picasso!

NEW MOM SHAMING

Along the same theme of judgment, have you ever felt bullied, could be either an aggressive way or passive, because of your parenting choices? In current day language we often recognize this as mom shaming. More specifically I have come to recognize new mom shaming, which is similar but directed toward first-time parents who are working through the way they want to parent; most often shamed by someone with a little more experience behind them. You may be extra diligent about something and a more seasoned mom points out how much you are worrying over nothing. Or you may be told that you are doing things wrong, because a first time mom doesn't know any better. These interactions breach the support between mothers, even though that support is truly needed in our communities. It is important that we recognize and support other mothers for the challenges they are facing, even if someone else's challenges are not something we may directly relate to.

I can recount a few of instances of new mom shaming I fell victim to. On one particular occasion when we were attending a wedding the music was blaring to levels of uncharted decibels, so I put noise-cancelling headphone on Matteo and he managed to fall asleep in my arms while everyone else was on the dance floor. Though I did not mind this whatsoever and enjoyed the cuddles and resting in my chair, another mom scooped Matteo out of my arms, ripped off his headphones, exclaimed I was being way too neurotic as a new mother, and insisted I put him down in his stroller so I could go have fun with all the other adults.

I can understand her intentions trying to talk me out of my nervousness and I did my best to not be offended by her actions or suggestions. But what seasoned moms forget is the empathy for where we are at in our parenting journey. There is a difference in the way a new mom processes her decisions as a mother versus someone who's already been through it. Seasoned moms already got to live through that first time. They have endured through the battle. They have been in enemy fire and survived it. We, as new moms, haven't. We are still navigating new and foreign territory using trial and error. Once we are successful at keeping our babies alive for the first year, then maybe we can reflect on our parenting choices and know we have done something right. Or know that we did something wrong and, in the grand scheme of things, it wasn't such a big deal. Once we live through our little one bumping their head or catching a cold, then our next go around at this parenting thing isn't as much uncharted territory to navigate through. (Yes, I do believe my comparison of going into battle and raising a baby is quite fitting, and, no, I don't think I am being melodramatic).

A BUTTLOAD OF OPTIONS

The last point I want to touch on regarding the power of choice is the anxiety that can be brought about for the mere reason we are given a buttload of options. A ton of research on this idea has proven a recipe for anxiety and depression; it is known as the paradox of choice.[38] This means that satisfaction in life declines when options increase because we become heightened to the opportunities we've given up or that we may be missing out on. The more options we have in front of us creates anxiety in the fact that when we pick a path we don't know if we have chosen the right one or if we would be happier doing something different. To lighten the load of this conversation, in a very superficial and insignificant example in life, have you ever been to a restaurant to only wallow in the endless choices on the menu? Ahh, how are you ever supposed to choose? And when you do choose, you may catch yourself glancing back at the menu pondering if you made the right decision or if that lobster mac and cheese was the right way to go. Oh man, you definitely should have gotten the mac and cheese. Always choose the lobster mac, you will never be disappointed. Sorry I was starting to get hungry, now back to my point.

On the other side of things have you ever been to a restaurant that is legendary for one thing and one thing only? For instance, they are an infamous burger joint. Their menu is small because they just focus on making the juiciest burgers they can. Maybe you need to add some guacamole to it or hold the tomatoes, but you are at the restaurant specifically for that mouth-watering double patty. The choice is really not so hard and you leave the restaurant belly full and mind happy, not ever second-guessing your dinner selection.

Making decisions in the parenting world can bring about this same type of paradox. This day-and-age of parenting offers so many options to any one decision our minds are inundated with confusion, doubt, and uncertainty; we are never quite sure if we are making the right decision or have done the absolute best job as a parent. Is it the right choice for your family? Would life be better for your baby if you did 'this' differently or 'that' differently? When you are feeling overwhelmed with choices, utilize the strategy in this chapter to think through those important decisions, be cognizant of the values you want to live by and remind yourself the most vital part of it all — the end goal — will allow the things that don't matter so much to take a back seat.

AS A NEW MOM SHIT HAPPENS, A LOT, AND IN MORE WAYS THAN ONE

-Kristy P.

Mom to Matteo and Baby #2 on the way

10
ARE WE ALL JUST A BUNCH OF IMPOSTERS?

Oh, the Mom Guilt!

MOM guilt. Oh, that dang mom guilt! Don't fool yourselves, ladies, you will experience it. I would say an average of about 567 times a day. Mom guilt is characterized by this overpowering, gut-wrenching feeling of regret over something we did or didn't do that *we think* has failed our children. It may be the feeling you get when you drop your baby off at daycare and then head to your job. Time away from your child and having someone else be responsible for them is enough for anyone to feel some level of guilt as a parent, especially in the early stages of their life. Maybe you bumped your baby's head on the side of the door frame on the way out of the house. Has your baby ever gotten a diaper rash because you waited a little too long before changing their diaper? Realized their lunch consisted of two cookies and nothing else? Yup, that's always accompanied by a side of mom guilt. Kept them in the car seat for four hours while running your errands without a break? Noticed a scratch on their face because you forgot to cut their nails that morning? You guessed it: mom guilt. Mom guilt. Mom guilt. This is known to occur in working moms, single moms, married moms, stay-at-home moms, young moms, old moms... you get the picture. Every kind of mom experiences it.

Mom guilt is a product of the doubt we feel in our capabilities. We feel this uncertainty because we second-guess our parenting abilities. And, for whatever reason, it's human nature to focus on any type of wrongdoing than to celebrate our mom wins. Maybe it's the universe's way of keeping us all humble. You can dwell on the fact that you forgot the organic bananas for your baby's smoothie today, but never took the time to pat yourself on the back for that hour-long dance party you entertained them with as they giggled away.

This is also known as Imposter Syndrome; the idea that you don't deserve your achievements, you worry that someone will expose your inability, and that you are a *fraud*. More specifically, Imposter Mom Syndrome is the thought that we don't feel that we know enough about mothering to be a mother, so we don't trust ourselves. Even when there is no reason not to. There is this belief out there that we are wired to be textbook parents[39] and that our capabilities are born alongside our child. I have to tell you a secret: all new moms feel this way and there isn't a single mom out there that knows everything about parenthood.

What is considered the right way to parent is constructed in a variety of ways such as gender conditioning so often experienced in early childhood.[40] These expectations are internalized early on in life and when a woman reaches motherhood, the vision they had for themselves as a mother may not become their reality.[41] So, when we do enter motherhood and realize it's just one big learning curve, we feel as though we aren't living up to the expectation that we set for ourselves. Interestingly, Imposter Mom Syndrome is especially prevalent among women considered to be high-achievers; also a common trait in mothers who battle mental health disorders because such personalities generally set high expectations for themselves. Understanding that this is an inherent trait in certain individuals is not meant to place blame on the individual for any type of negativity brought into their life, but rather gives us hope that we can better recognize risk factors when it comes to maternal mental health. If you suffer from Imposter Syndrome, one simple strategy to help you overcome these feelings is to **focus on, and document, any achievement you experience and then take the time to celebrate it.**[42] Build confidence in yourself by having proof (because it is there, I promise) that you are winning at this parenting thing.

A CHALLENGE FOR YOU

Anytime you are quick to judge a "screw up" you did as a mom, take a moment to identify two things you did successfully that same day. To take this one step further, anytime you are quick to judge *another* mom's "screw up", acknowledge two things she did great. Tell her these achievements you witnessed and spread that kindness and support.

Let's remind ourselves that our mom guilt comes from our overpowering love for our children. For most of us, mom guilt doesn't stem from our worry about how others view us. It comes from us wanting to do everything in our power to give our children their best life, their best potential, and do anything we can to rid them of hurt or harm. Let's acknowledge it and understand it, but don't be debilitated by it.

I want you to listen to me very carefully. Sooner or later, as a mom, you are going to fuck up (I felt compelled to drop an 'F-bomb' here, I apologize, it just seemed so fitting). You are going to make mistakes. And that's okay!

I locked my four-month-old in the car.

You think it won't happen to you... until it does.

It was a hot summer's day. We had just finished up at a baptism and about to head home when Matteo needed a diaper change. I decided to change him in the back seat of my car, which seemed easier than lugging everything back into the church. I finished up and loaded him into his car seat. As I got out of the back, the door closed behind me, followed by a *Beep-Beep*.

In car language *Beep-Beep* means *I have taken it upon myself to lock every single door of your vehicle without your permission; you are welcome.* I peered through the window to see my set of car keys in the back seat. Now to make matters worse, my husband and I — in the chaos of leaving the house on time — both grabbed a set of keys; the only two keys we owned to that car were locked inside. Along with my four-month-old.

My first instinct was to... well... puke, to be frank. My second: put my fist through the window. Luckily, my husband grabbed my arm mid-punch and was able to talk some sense into me.

We called Roadside Assist and when you scream to the lady on the other end "MY CHILD IS LOCKED IN MY CAR" ('F-bombs' removed here) you somehow get priority.

Luckily, they opened the door without any difficulty and Matteo was just fine. I think he might have slept through all of the mayhem.

But that point forward, I knew I wasn't invincible as a mom. I had heard similar horror stories from my friends:

"Ben rolled off the bed and hit his head."

"Sam contracted an eye infection and had to be admitted to the hospital."

"Zoey had an allergic reaction to peanuts and we had to call the ambulance."

I heard these stories, I felt sick for those moms, but I hadn't personally experienced something so scary. Until I locked Matteo in the car on a hot summer day. Now each night before I go to bed I count my blessings knowing we got through another day without anything too Earth-shattering occurring within the last 24 hours.

I know I am not the first — or the last — mother to lock her child in the car, but if you asked me a year ago, I would never guess that such a thing would happen to me. From that, I lost about ten points off my mom confidence-o-meter, which brought me into that "fraud" rating of my mothering skills. "When is someone going to realize I do not know what I am doing?" I kept thinking to myself. So, I tried to remind myself that I have the ability to win those points back tomorrow. But, oh man, that mom guilt I experienced was *real*!

Coincidentally, in the midst of me writing this chapter, just this morning Matteo hit his head pretty dang hard from a fall when I was watching him. At this moment in time, my stomach is only slowly making its way down from my throat, where it has been residing all day. I tell you these stories, hoping you aren't picking up the phone to call the Child Protective Services on me, the unfit mother, but instead to tell you the god-honest truth that these things happen. And in some way-shape-or-form, they will happen again.

My mom, a mother of four, shared a story with me that when my sister was only nine months old, with my Grandma, two Aunts, and my mom all watching her take her first steps she walked straight toward the stove and burnt both her hands on the scorching oven door. While four adults watched it happen! After taking her into the emergency department, the doctor announced my sister would never have fingerprints again. Looking back on it, I guess it isn't the worst thing in the world if she wanted to live a life of a bank robber. My mom and dad were then taken to separate rooms and thoroughly questioned to rule out child abuse. Did my mom have mom guilt, you ask? Did she question her capabilities as a parent? To this day, she thinks of that story and cringes, and that happened 35 years ago. But my mom, if you ever need to pick someone's brain on this topic, has countless shutter-worthy stories of raising four rambunctious children and she, and all her children, survived to tell the tale.

To be clear, my mother is the be-all of mothers. She's kind, intuitive, safe, and I know for a fact she has eyes in the back of her head. So, when I am having a bad day (like today when Matteo hit his head on the tile floor) I need her to remind me that it happens to the best of us, it happens to all of us, and it's going to be okay. If you need a Mama like mine in your life, I will give you her phone number and she can talk you off the mommy guilt ledge at any time of the day.

Do you know who else talked me off the ledge? My support group of other mothers because who knows mom guilt better than all the other moms who are raising a baby alongside you? If you need a reminder of this, go back to chapter 3.

I am going to tell you one more time, we *will* fuck up (last 'F-bomb' I promise), we will have those off-days and we may make the wrong judgement call once or twice on any given day.

Remember your intentions are always in the right place and you are capable. You aren't trying to hurt your baby; your entire existence is about keeping them safe and thriving. But remember, we are human and things happen. That gut-wrenching mom guilt in the pit of your stomach is all the evidence you need to remind yourself that you are the best mom ever. Because. You. Care.

IT'S HARD. IT'S HARD AS HELL, BUT, YOU WILL GET THROUGH IT

-Sabrina F.

Mom to Milan

11
BECOMING YOUR OWN BODYGUARD

Managing your Influences

HAVE you ever watched a really scary horror movie that keeps you up all night; you know, with nightmares about being chased through a corn maze or constantly wondering if someone is lurching behind your door? Does it cross your mind how much we are affected by what we allow to enter into our being? Horror movies are the mere start of it and only one small, maybe even trivial, example. For some, you may not even blink twice at the Exorcist or Jason. But what about your social media feed? Does what you scroll through ever overpower your thoughts throughout the day? What about all those questions you type into your Google search bar? The six o'clock news? What about your negative-Nancy co-worker that you go out for lunch with every day? Throughout our daily lives, we are constantly being bombarded with influences that bring up emotions in us that may be constructive or — on the flip side — damaging to our well-being. Being in a vulnerable state, such as the transition into motherhood when you may not feel resilient as you fight through sleep deprivation, pain, trying to heal while being overwhelmed with responsibilities and hormones, what you expose yourself to can take an even greater toll on your mental health.

So, I ask you, what are you allowing into your life that isn't adding to your resiliency? Think about what you watch, listen to, follow, who you speak to, whatever it may be that adversely influences your feelings after your interaction. Jay Shetty, a former monk and the author of *Think like a Monk*, talks about the media mind game: "...The mind is the vehicle by which we decide what is important in our hearts. The movies we watch, the music we hear, the books we read, the TV shows we binge, the people we follow online and offline. What's on your news feed is feeding your mind. The more we are absorbed in celebrity gossip, images of success, violent video games, and troubling news, the more our values are tainted with envy, judgement, competition, and discontent. . . **When we tune out the opinions, expectations, and obligations of the world around us, we begin to hear ourselves."**[43] Jay's thoughts are even further supported by research that suggests that the action as simple as scrolling through your friend's Facebook page and feeling envy has a direct correlation to depression.[44]

To add to our understanding of why mothers with a new baby are deeply affected by exposure to certain things, we must talk about the role our hormones play into this. It is proven that the release of oxytocin actually increases our ability to read faces and emotions; it enhances our proficiency to pick up on social cues, making us hypersensitive to those around us. Even the slightest of cues may be off-putting. Instinctually, this heightened state we enter aids us in our ability to interact with our babies and to respond to their needs, but it plays a role in *all* the interactions we are exposed to.[45] Which means there's even more to it than our daily intake of media we talked about above. A very monumental influence on our well-being is the people in our lives. Sometimes these are people we choose to bring into our circle and sometimes it's not our choice, such as family, co-workers, or even our neighbours. Of course, we cannot completely avoid interactions with negative people and we most certainly cannot control how others interact with, or respond to, us. But you may have a little more control over this influence than you think in some situations.

Though we cannot avoid certain individuals, we can limit our exposure when we feel it is detrimental to our well-being. For instance, abiding by a strict timeline for your visit may be important for you. Set a maximum amount of time you spend with your company and then when the time is up, no matter what the circumstances, say your good-byes and depart. Advise them beforehand that you will need to leave by a certain time so that there are no surprises when you start heading toward the exit. Too much time with particular people can sometimes weaken boundaries and cause rifts in relationships or lead to unpleasant interactions. Know your limits.

In other circumstances, acknowledge when you aren't feeling rested or resilient and avoid interactions altogether. There is no harm in rescheduling a coffee date with your sister-in-law if you know her comments always seem to cut a little deep and you were up all night with a crying baby. Though you may value a relationship with your family member, you are entitled to off-days and supporting your mental health should be higher on your priority list than appeasing others with a visit. You don't need to be available for everyone in your life all the time because, if you are, that means there is never a time you are looking out for your well-being over others. This needs to happen sometimes.

A CHALLENGE FOR YOU

In a 24-hour period, keep track and list out everything you spent time focusing on: television shows, the people you conversed with, your social media feed and online influences, etc. Beside each, write down how you felt after the interaction. Is what you're focusing on and putting your energy toward helping or hindering your well-being? Do you have an abundance of constructive influences, or are most of them unhealthy? You may recognize feelings such as: stressed, worn out, panicked, drained, apathetic, sad, etc. Or, hopefully, you may identify positive feelings such as: uplifted, joyful, silly, strong, confident, inspired, etc. Were you aware of these influences before this exercise? Are you more self-aware after seeing on paper *what* you are allowing to affect you and *how* it is affecting you? Now I ask you: how can you change your daily habits to decrease feelings that feed into your angst?

Your eyes are the windows into your soul. This means that your truth will be shown to the world through your eyes. The pain, the wisdom, the joy you feel are no secret to the world; just by looking into your eyes all is revealed. Being the philosopher that I like to think I am, let's take this expression one step further. If our eyes are the windows into our soul and windows are transparent on both sides, then not only are we projecting our truth out into the world, but **we are also exposing our**

souls to the truth of the world. So, I ask you, what is your truth that you are teaching your soul? Let's protect that one-and-only psyche we are blessed with in this lifetime and manage the influence that we reveal to her.

It's an impossible task to think we can live a life in which every interaction, every situation, everything we watch or listen to will benefit us, but it doesn't have to be. The point of this strategy is to be more cognizant of what we expose ourselves to and after that last challenge exercise maybe you've become more aware of how much control you can gain back in this aspect of your life. We aren't ignorant enough to believe the world is only rainbows-and-butterflies, or even that it needs to be. This is us knowing we, as new moms searching for our new identity, are conscious of our triggers that bring negativity, anxiety, and sadness in.

TOXIC POSITIVITY & EMOTIONAL AGILITY

Speaking of rainbows-and-butterflies, let's talk about toxic positivity. Toxic positivity is "the overgeneralization of a happy, optimistic state that results in the denial, minimization, and invalidation of the authentic human emotional experience."[46] In other words, even when things are shit, we pretend as though it's cake.

Toxic positivity is this unrealistic view that everything, no matter what the circumstance, *is* wonderful and *should always be* wonderful. That no matter what you are going through in life, you should just have a positive mindset. If someone is sad about being fired from their job, a toxic reply would be "well it could be worse;" such a response doesn't validate the sadness that person feels and is entitled to feel. We have all met people like that, haven't we? In reality, as much as it's great to try and put a positive spin on things, it is actually healthier for our well-being to identify those feelings of sadness — that are warranted! — and work through them. It's a fine line between a positive outlook and toxic positivity. We already learned early in this book there are feelings of sadness, a sense of loss, confusion, and pain in motherhood that we can experience, even when we may be told we have nothing to complain about and should be grateful for our wonderful babies. It is okay to recognize all those feelings and then spend the time to process them. Understand them for what they are and acknowledge all the things that are forever changed in your life, *even though* you are blessed with a child.

So, how can we acknowledge these feelings — our own or someone else's — and properly process them or support someone to do the same?

Susan David is an author and psychologist that coined the term emotional agility. This refers to the action of being more in touch with our feelings, honouring our feelings, and then working through them. She states that "emotional agility is an individual's ability to experience their thoughts and emotions and events in a way that doesn't drive them in negative ways, but instead encourages them to reveal the best of themselves."[47] It gives us the skills to understand a better sense of what motivates us, affects us, and how we react to situations.

Let's discuss a few key concepts from Susan that can help us work toward emotional agility:

- *Face your real feelings*: We must first learn when we are getting hooked by our thoughts or our feelings, meaning we need to recognize when our thinking becomes rigid or repetitive. This is how we know we are 'stuck' by our feelings before we can even try to make a change. Once we acknowledge the emotions we are feeling, we need to face them instead of ignore them, even though it may make us uncomfortable.

- *Detach from your emotions:* Secondly, we need to label those repetitive thoughts or feelings. Labeling them means identifying them for exactly what they are: simply a thought or a feeling. Instead of, "I am angry when my baby cries" try, "I feel angry when my baby cries" — it's that simple! This is a mindfulness practice that aids us in using our emotions to gain insight and understanding of what we are feeling, so that we can do something about them. Though this step may seem ineffective, it helps us to detach from our emotions, knowing they are merely feelings we have and not actually who we are (Sound familiar? Reminder here of chapter 7 and the ideals behind the practice of non-attachment). From there look at the emotion you have identified. Is angry your true feeling? Maybe a better explanation of your emotion could be "I feel overwhelmed when my baby cries." Taking the time to step away from the emotion will help you identify what it is you are truly feeling.
- *Match your feelings to your core values:* Emotions can be a source of productivity that can offer you a push toward change based on what you acknowledge you are feeling. Here we need to act on our emotions by aligning them with our values. Just as we discussed in chapter 9, we can make decisions for our family when we recognize what's important to us.
- *Set your goals:* When you have feelings toward something that is constantly taking up space in your mind, use this as a chance to spark change and better live a life in

alignment with what you care about. Ask yourself how you can purposefully follow through on habits that will support your journey to feel more mentally healthy.[48]

WHAT ABOUT THOSE UNHEALTHY HABITS WE USE TO DEAL WITH OUR EMOTIONS?

Now, what about unhealthy ways to process emotions? An improper, but widely-used habit in North America is the use of alcohol, or sometimes drugs, to treat negative emotions we may feel. This practice is correlated to high incidences of anxiety or depression, so I feel the need to talk about why such options are unproductive remedies to deal with our thoughts or feelings. It can be confusing because alcohol and drugs can make us feel "better" but let me explain why this is just a façade.

Anxiety and depression in our minds are similar to a big hole in a wall; it's ugly and obvious and no matter where you are in that room that hole can catch your attention. You may do your best to ignore it, but it is always there and it is not going to miraculously disappear on its own. The only way to get rid of such an unpleasantry is to do some labour. That hole needs to be filled with plaster, meticulously sanded down and painted over. It is labour-intensive, takes time, and is hard work. Just as with anxiety and depression there is no quick fix. You also cannot pretend as though you are an expert in carpentry and fix the hole unless you have been taught the skills to do so properly. If it's not done right, even after the repaired hole is painted, the patchwork will be obvious. It takes experts and people in your corner that have the knowledge and strategies to help you manage anxiety and depression properly.

Alcohol and drugs, though, are that beautiful piece of art you decide to hang on the wall to hide the hole. It looks pretty and it even helps you to forget all about that big ugly cavity underneath. But don't be fooled: no matter how many Van Goghs you cover it with, the hole is still there. And as soon as that picture comes off the wall, that hole will be just as deep as before, staring back at you.

This "artwork" may give you a sense of a quick fix to your feelings of anxiety and depression; however, you may be confusing the *numbness* we feel with alcohol and drugs as the same thing as the *calmness* we are supposed to feel when we have a healthy mindset. Let's be cognizant these two feelings are not the same thing.

Don't get me wrong, I love to enjoy a glass of wine. I am not telling you that it's something you need to cut from your life — that is a personal decision. What I want you to take from this is why alcohol or drugs can be unhealthy if used as the antidote to fix our feelings of anxiety or depression, when that is what we are using it for. We must just look at it for what it is. And what it is not: solving our problems.

Managing your influences is a gigantic topic and is relevant to almost every part of our daily lives. We talked about the shows we watch, the people we scroll on social media platforms, and even the people we interact with. Knowing your triggers is just one more strategy toward working on your well-being and supporting your best self to transition into motherhood. There are so many situations, feelings, and experiences that are out of our control, but let's not avoid life. Instead, let's do our best to provide our soul with healthy influences that bring us up, rather than tears us down.

12
MY PRIORITY CHERRY PIE

Prioritizing your Endless Responsibilities

AS a mom, it's great to be productive. I mean, is there any other option? But let's talk about something a little more important: managing our expectations and being realistic about what we can truly manage to accomplish in 24 hours. When you become a parent and you have the very heavy responsibility of someone else's life in your hands, it's impossible to continue to do all the things you did in a day before having your baby.

I am sure you have heard the expression, "it takes a village to raise a baby." If you haven't, well then, I am here to tell you that **it takes a village to raise a baby**. When, I ask you, did we suddenly believe that we — all on our own — can be that entire village? We are the hunter, the gatherer, and the wise elder that knows the answer to all questions. We can heal our bodies while simultaneously running a household, grocery shopping, and whipping up photo-worthy meals for our families. We can scrub those toilets and iron those shirts like nobody's business, all the while looking like we walked straight off the runway at New York Fashion Week. Let us not forget that we are also the most doting daughter, picture-perfect wife, fun aunty, and the best friend anyone could ask for. We contribute to the household income and pay bills each month on time, all without skipping a beat. Sounds exhausting, doesn't it? Just the thought of all the responsibilities that pile up makes me want to hide under a rock most days.

This chapter is meant to give you an approach to life and it is my hope that it helps you prioritize tasks in a way that seems a little more manageable. Though we may all relate to one another on the new mom front, our day-to-day lives are different; we all have different values, responsibilities, and roles than the next, so to tell you how you are supposed to spend your time will not be constructive. The goal of this chapter is to offer you a simple strategy to bring into your world and make it work for you and your family. I like to refer to it as my priority pie of chaos.

My pie has a cherry filling, what flavour is yours?

To incorporate this analogy into our lives, let's first lay out its guidelines. This may not make too much sense right now, but we will come to reference these points throughout the chapter to wrap it all together:

1. Each day represents a fresh priority pie, and it is always prepped the night before.
2. Each pie will look different than the last.
3. Once you are "full", you must put your pie away, no matter how much of it is left. Some days you may devour it all, while other days you may struggle to finish half or even less. It

doesn't matter how much you finish; what matters is — as the saying goes — to never bite off more than you can chew.

4. Never divide your pie up into more than six slices.
5. At least one slice each day is meant to uplift you.
6. Be sure to eat a variety of slices to nurture yourself holistically.
7. Oh, and your priority pie is always zero calories, so no need to stress about point #3. Although, if I could figure out the recipe for an indulgent, zero-calorie cherry pie, I'd be switching over to writing cookbooks and probably be making a fortune by now.
8. Just so we are clear, you know by now that this is just an imaginary pie, right? I am not expecting you to bake a real pie each day. That would be one more thing for you to do and, on a chapter about endless responsibilities, that is just silly!

Now that we have a grasp on the concepts that make up our priority pie, let's go over how this exercise works: Let's start with guideline #1, we must always "prep" our pie the night before for the following day. This preparation will help to give you a sense of control when you are feeling overwhelmed with responsibilities. Feeling as though you have a *flexible* plan in place can offer you a bit of direction to follow when you wake up in the morning. It's too easy to jump out of bed to the cries of your baby, dirty diapers, and the dog needing to pee, and often you are behind on your day before you are given a fair start. Go to bed knowing — to some degree — what your schedule looks like. Remind yourself that worry and anxiety can increase when you feel as though you are not in charge of your life.

Part of the preparation of your pie is to cut that sucker into slices, but don't get too ahead of yourself, this is *the most* important part. Each piece is going to represent one priority for the next day, so the number of slices and size of each piece is significant. Write out the most essential tasks that you want to get accomplished the next day and allocate the importance and time needed to complete each one. Each piece of your pie should represent one of these tasks. It doesn't need to be an exact replication of your hours in a day; writing these out within your pie slices merely acts as a visual aid to show you how much of your energy must be dedicated to the responsibilities you have identified.

Your priority pie is comparable to a daily to-do list or a family calendar to guide you in what needs to get accomplished each day. The difference, though, is significant. This priority pie strategy teaches us that there is only so much we can do in a day, and it halts us from overloading on the expectations we set for ourselves. Drawing out this pie as one full circle and then allocating your tasks to pieces of the pie is the visual reminder we need that stops us from going overboard on our list of to-dos. If you are anything like me, your daily list of chores always require more time than there are minutes in a day and are very ambitious. Not only can I never get to the bottom of my list on any given day, but it also often discourages me. It's as if no matter how much I accomplish, I must always be functioning at 110%, or else I am failing at life.

This priority pie exercise is simple, it is meant to be! Draw out a circle, divide out your pieces, and identify your tasks for the following day. There is no point in complicating your life more because being a mom is difficult enough. *But* even though there is nothing too complex about your priority pie, there is still a good amount of knowledge you must gain to do this exercise *well*. When you get the hang of it, you may recognize there is a fine line between balancing your life responsibilities and knowing there are only so many priorities that will fit on your plate.

So how can we appropriately utilize this strategy in a way that will be beneficial to our day's organization? Well, first and foremost, to help you gauge what are realistic expectations for yourself and the slices you allocate, follow the advice from experts within the field of prioritization and organization: you should never have more than six priorities on any given day,[49] which corresponds to #4 in our guideline. This means you are never going to divide your pie up into more than six pieces. Ever.

Less than six?

Good on you! The goal here is not to get as many things done in a day as humanly possible; instead, we are learning to balance our responsibilities and make sensible expectations for ourselves.

Secondly, we need to determine what priorities hold enough weight to take up an entire slice of our pie each day and this part of the exercise takes a little more explaining.

To give you a background on this, it was when I began to feel as though I was drowning in all my responsibilities that I felt the need to do this exercise. Prior to strategizing my daily priority pie of chaos, I would think of my jam-packed days and wonder how I was going to manage it all, while simultaneously *trying* to stay sane. There came a point when minuscule tasks, such as clipping my toenails or sending out birthday cards, felt comparable to climbing Mount Everest. Feeling quite concerned about my thoughts (did I really just compare shaping my nails to climbing the largest mountain in the world?!), I asked myself some questions to figure a way to better manage the responsibilities that just kept piling up:

- How do I get through my to-do list when there aren't enough hours in a day?
- If I have come to realize I can't do it all, how can I figure a way to live a life that supports what is important to me?
- How much should I expect from myself as a new mom and when am I pushing myself to a point that is unhealthy for my well-being?
- Oh, and is there ever going to be a way to fit some time in a day for **me**?

To figure out what priorities are going to make it onto your pie each day, let's answer these questions.

How do I get through my to-do list when there aren't enough hours in a day?

This answer is simple: **we don't need to do it all in a day**. We can prioritize and do our best, but I promise you that life will go on even if you don't manage to finish everything you thought you would. Remember, too, that babies can be unpredictable. You may think you have a flawless schedule planned for the following day, until your nugget keeps you up all that night, completely abandoning their regular nighttime routine. These extra challenges can wear us down considerably. Recognize those unexpected challenges we are faced with and alter the expectations you had placed on yourself. Make friends with flexibility.

To choose what is important enough to get to ask yourself where your task falls:

- Is it *urgent and important*? These tasks can take up a slice of your pie.
- Is it *important* but *not urgent*? Depending on how your day is

looking, these tasks might be a slice of our pie, or scheduled in for another day soon.

- Is it *urgent* but *not important*? These are the types of tasks that could be delegated to someone else to help you get checked off your list.
- Neither *urgent nor important*? Cut these out and don't give them a slice of your pie, until you have the extra time and energy to do so and when you don't mind putting it towards this task. Until then, adios! Remember, these types of tasks probably don't add much value to your life.[50]

If I have come to realize I can't do it all, how can I figure a way to live a life that supports what is important to me?

To answer this question, I have a challenge for you.

A CHALLENGE FOR YOU

Spend a few days tracking where you spend your time. This will give you an idea of how much of your day you are devoting to the responsibilities in your life including family, friends, health, home, work, yourself, etc. Recognizes that "the areas where you spend the most time should match what you value the most."[51]

After doing this exercise, it was apparent to me that I was a little out of whack with my prioritization of housework. Though I valued a clean home, I realized that it was taking away so much of my cherished playtime with Matteo, which is something I value so much more than smudge-free windows. It wasn't until I tracked my time that this truth was staring me in the face. Cleaning every square inch of my kitchen right after we finished supper didn't seem quite as crucial anymore. Now, as I am writing this chapter, I can see out of the corner of my eye the avocado Matteo decided to throw across the kitchen and onto my cupboard doors. He loved avocado yesterday but decided he hates it today, so it ended up encrusted onto my cabinets instead of in his tummy. Though some of you may gasp at the thought of caked-on food on your kitchen cabinets, and I too hate that it's there, I have learned that it's only one small conundrum in the grand scheme of our busy lives. I've learned to accept it may be there for a little while longer before I take the time to scrape it all away. The point is, if I felt the need to scrape the food off my cupboards and maintain an absolutely perfect household as my top priority every day, I would never find the time to take Matteo swimming each week, watch him take his first steps, or do somethings for myself — like write this book! This exercise helped me alter my priorities to better support my true values and this story sums up my motherhood reality in two simple words: Avocado. Everywhere.

Now let's take this challenge one step further.

The next part is to then identify and link each task to a particular type of energy. Let me explain:

There are four major categories of human energy: physical, emotional, spiritual, and mental. Though there is much overlap within these energy types, certain tasks can pinpoint a particular energy and deplete it or, on the other hand, build it back up. Physical energy is the most understood human energy and can exhaust under tasks such as exercising, heavy lifting, or housework. Our mental energy is what we burn when we are learning something new, studying, working, or making difficult decisions, for example. Emotional energy is related to our feelings of happiness and joy. Depleting our emotional energy is caused by internal or external conflict, such as: ruminating about past events, worrying about the future, or having an argument with someone. Lastly, spiritual energy is linked to why you are doing what you are doing or, in other words, your purpose in life. Feelings of connection with other things, such as your connection to other people, to nature, and to a higher power can support your spiritual energy while a disconnect can diminish it. I was once told that when you are living against your true values, it's exhausting. Now that I have a better understanding of these energy types, I see the truth in such a statement because living against your values is diminishing your spiritual energy. Simply put, productive rest and recovery (in different forms) is vital to replenishing all our human energies.

For the vast majority of us, we have a basic understanding of physical energy, but our awareness stops there. When we feel drained even without days of physical labour, we may feel a sense of confusion. We may not grasp that an unwanted phone call or argument with a friend could be the cause for the exhaustion we feel. Unfortunately, this is usually why we push ourselves harder; we believe that if we haven't done anything physically strenuous in a day, then why would we need to slow down and rest?

What's more, we all burn these energies differently and this is the reason why our priority pies are so individually focused. Taking your dog for a walk could be spiritually uplifting or it could be physically draining. It could also be both, remembering these energies have an interconnection with one another. Depending on your relationships, your emotional energy could be either supported or weakened through your daily interactions. Your job may not be mentally stimulating, but it could feel physically and spiritually draining. If we sat down together with our priority pies in hand, even if our slices looked identical, our energies would be burning differently based on our personalities. The significance of learning about our four energy types is it may help us look internally to better understand what is wearing on us. It takes a lot of self-awareness, but having this insight can be life-changing. So, once you have recognized where you are spending your time, consider how each activity impacts your physical, emotional, mental, and spiritual energy.

As we wrap this back to supporting our optimal mental health, it's important to speak on the energy we expend through the worry and angst that comes with anxiety and depression. Though we can understand that the energy spent dwelling about things is exhausting, it's also not so simple to just stop worrying when you are depressed or anxious. So, let's find a compromise. A common technique taught by many therapists is to schedule "worry time" into your day, which, depending on your needs, may mean this could be a slice of your pie. Allocate 30 minutes to your day to focus on those thoughts and when your alarm goes off you are done. If your mind wanders back to these thoughts later on in the day, tell yourself you don't have any more time in the day to worry because you have already finished that slice of your pie!

If you take the time to complete this challenge, I am hopeful you will have a better consideration of what types of tasks are important to you and, in turn, give them the slice of pie they deserve.

This also brings us back to our guideline, specifically point #6: your pie slices should be as balanced as possible amongst the four energy types. You should attempt to dedicate time to as many of the four energies on any given day, instead of over-focusing on one. For me, for example, I have learned that I cannot overload on physical chores, the same day I push Matteo in his stroller and go for a five-kilometer run. Both are too physically exerting and will tire me out much faster than splitting up these two tasks on different days. Instead, I plan my run on a day that is a little less physically daunting around the house.

This takes us to #2 of our priority pie guideline: each day your pie is going to look different because, as you may have thought, there are so many responsibilities and only six slices per day. It may feel impossible to ever stay on track with life, but when we understand how we are affected by our tasks at hand (physically, emotionally, mentally, and spiritually), we can switch our focus each day to find a balance between how we are exerting ourselves, how we can recharge, and how to still feel productive.

How much should I expect from myself as a new mom and when am I pushing myself to a point that is unhealthy for my well-being?

I recently read, in a book about caring for others and expectations we place on ourselves, that "[we] have the right to do less than [we] are humanly capable of doing."[52] For whatever reason, this was a belief I held on to for so long; I must give my absolute all every single day. It's interesting to think that it took me to see those words written down, as if they gave me permission, before I realized that I had that right to not do *everything I am humanly capable of all the time*. So let this advice permit you to sometimes take a breather without feeling any guilt.

On the same topic, there is a saying in Okinawa, Japan (one of the few blue zone regions in the world that represent some of the healthiest and oldest living population); *"Hara Hachi bu"* which means, stop eating when you are 80% full.[53]Although this advice is dedicated to living longer through healthier eating practices, being the foodie that I am, I say that this applies to our mental health just the same! This supports point #3 in our guideline: stop when you're 80% "full" and when you have had enough for one day, put your tasks list away. Practicing this will keep us and our well-being healthier. No longer are the days you expend your energy to the point you are so tired that the thought of putting your pajamas over your head before you crawl into bed for the night is too much. No matter how many of the priorities you cross off your list, when you think you are done, be done! There will be days you get through your entire pie and still feel great, other days it may only be a couple of slices before you are exhausted. On those days, the rest of your pie will have to wait for another day and that is just fine. This means you adjust your priorities the following day around what is important to carry forward from the previous day and what is necessary for tomorrow. Don't get discouraged, I promise you there will be days you can handle much more than other days. Continue to focus on that self-awareness, listen to your body, and stop when it's time to stop.

Is there ever going to be a way to fit some time in a day for ***me****?*

There was a time shortly after becoming a mother that I realized I was never offering a space for *me* in my day (reminder here of chapter 6: self-care). I was the last priority to everything — and everyone — else. Whatever the task on any given day, it was always more important than the time set aside for some self-love. So, with a little insight from my husband (if you recall, he was the one that forced me to spend a day at the spa) I decided that it doesn't have to be this way and it shouldn't be this way. I can, and should, make myself a priority and to do so meant I must dedicate a slice of my pie to Kristy.

The priorities we identify each day should not only be chores or those dreadful tasks we just have to get done. Prioritize you. Prioritize your rest, physical activity, or any other self-care options that help you recharge, and write it down as one of your pie slices. This brings us to point #5: each pie should carry at least one slice that is meant to uplift you. Determine one priority each day that, when completed, will help you refill your physical, emotional, spiritual, or mental well-being tank.

MY PRIORITY CHERRY PIE OF CHAOS

It is true that many of our daily tasks, though daunting, are a part of life. This strategy has stopped me from thinking that I need to be on top of it all. A little bit each day keeps me afloat and that's all I ask of myself anymore. Like I mentioned at the very beginning of this exercise, I don't want to tell you how to spend your time, but I do want you to become cognizant of what is important to you and then balance out those roles and responsibilities to better support your well-being.

More often than not, we can't predict where we will need to expend our energy, we will be flexible as life throws us those curveballs and that is what makes this exercise so important. It offers us a little sense of control through preparation with the understanding that life is full of the unexpected.

ANOTHER CHALLENGE FOR YOU

Since there is always more to do in our busy lives, I challenge you to find a way to pass off one of your responsibilities. As often as possible, share a piece of your priority pie with someone else. To do so, you may need to get a little creative. Maybe you ask your neighbour's daughter to walk your dog for you. Maybe one night each week you order take-out for dinner. Maybe it means hiring a cleaning service once a month. Or getting your sister to come over and tend to your garden. You could hire a snow removal service (if you live in the Arctic like me) or a dog pooper-scooper company, which, by the way, is worth every penny. Try though to avoid passing off to anyone who also has a newborn; which means don't go directly to your significant other all the time. Look for outside sources.

It also shouldn't always have to cost money. Your neighbour's daughter who walked your dog, next time you bake a batch of muffins bring some over to her. Or maybe, just maybe, the person you have reached out to for help has read this book and will simply offer a helping hand with nothing expected in return, knowing where you are at in life raising a young baby.

Asking for help should no longer feel like a luxury in life, or that we aren't entitled to such support since every other mom is doing what we are doing. Instead, we should *all* be asking for help! Know that as I am writing this I, too, am just as guilty as ever for feeling this way. But, as I put this chapter away and go prep my priority pie for tomorrow, I will remind myself as I cut each slice that I no longer need to feel that I am responsible to do it all.

13
LET'S GET PHYSICAL!

Give your Body What She Needs

IN a book dedicated to mental health and well-being, it should come as no surprise that the strategies thus far have been fixated around strengthening our psychological processes, our outlook, and our mindset. But I would like to shift the focus for just a moment and give some of the spotlight to our physical body. Specifically, let's focus on our mind-body connection and speak to the influence that our physical health can have on our mental well-being.

Our bodies are truly and utterly amazing. Like superhero amazing. I find our ability to create human life, bring it into the world, and nourish it much more exciting than shooting spider webs from a wrist or extraterrestrial strength. Maybe it's time to have a Marvel movie about *that* kind of superpower. But, if you remember my miscarriage story, there was a point in time

I was wholeheartedly furious at my body. Furious for failing my baby; failing to provide her with the protection she needed to thrive, and offering her the necessities to grow big and strong. I blamed my body for this unimaginable loss and the guilt I felt every day.

It wasn't until I started practicing daily gratitude that I was able to change this perspective. There were many days I would write "my body" on my list as one of my three daily blessings. I had two working legs and a healthy strong heart. When I started to seek out the little things in life that I would generally overlook, I came to realize the hard work my body was doing every day to keep me alive and well. To take something as powerful as that for granted was a mindset I forced myself to change.

When I got pregnant for the second time, it became especially apparent to me how much I needed to acknowledge my body for the vessel she is and what she is capable of. When I experienced even the most unpleasant of pregnancy symptoms — retching into the toilet or the excessive swelling in my feet — I would be reminded of what that meant to my growing fetus. As I continued on my pregnancy journey and I began to experience Matteo kicking my ribs or doing somersaults in my belly, I would take the time to relish in such a special feeling and be grateful that it was my body responsible for such a gift.

Before rolling your eyes at me acting as though I was excited to upchuck my entire breakfast each morning, I will tell you that I found pregnancy extremely challenging, but who's not up for a good challenge? I learned to be grateful for it, yes, but it was not an easy experience for me. To paint you a picture of my gravidity, my husband nicknamed me "The Puffer Fish" because the swelling I had was a little, let's just say, over-the-top. Do you know those fish that have the ability to inflate like a balloon to about five times their size? If you have ever played Super Mario

Bros. you may recognize them in the underwater levels, when you get just a little too close and they expand to the point they will literally kill you?! That was me. By my third trimester, it took a supportive waistband, compression stockings, Crocs on my feet — only Crocs could fit — and icepacks on my hands to get me through my days at work. Each day my body felt as though it had been through the wringer. But as I look back on everything I went through and the end result of holding Matteo in my arms, I am grateful for such an accomplishment; I am indebted for the life *my body* created.

So after everything my body did for me, and the incredible changes she endured, how did I repay her? Well, I gave her a mere six weeks to recover before I felt the need to bounce right back into my old ways. I wanted to look the same, feel the same, and be just as physically capable as I was nine months prior. Common knowledge is, and we are told over and over, that we need six weeks of recovery after delivering a baby. Then from there, we are entirely rehabilitated from the hell our bodies suffered through. I will be honest, working as a maternity nurse I would tell my patients the same thing. "Just wait six weeks and then back to heavy lifting, exercising, sex, and whatever else you did prior. Nothing off limits!"

That, my friends, is complete bullshit.

Here we are recovering after months and months of creating and sustaining life, living through and mending from the physical delivery of giving birth (Caesarean section or vaginal birth — both need recovery), producing nourishment and feeding our littles ones on a very stringent schedule, on top of hormonal fluctuations, stress, sleep deprivation, and an entirely new daily routine. Our bodies really cannot catch a break, can they? Yet, we are told to believe that we have healed entirely within a measly six weeks.

Though it sounds ridiculous to admit now, after the birth of Matteo I couldn't count down fast enough to be back to my old self. I went as far as scheduling a workout on the exact date that marked six weeks following my delivery. When that day came, I woke up bright and early, more enthusiastic than ever to finally have my old self back, fully recovered to the human I identified as for the last 30 years of my life. The same self I felt had been "on vacation" for the last six weeks. Enough sitting around, let's get to it because I was, well, healed now wasn't I? I no longer had any excuses — I felt — to prioritize my rest and recovery.

Well, I kid you not, within minutes of stepping foot into the gym on that very first day I pulled my back out.

Looking back, I was unaware of how my expectations were influencing my behaviour. I am ashamed to admit those were the thoughts going through my head on day 42 of motherhood; my thoughts constantly focused on wanting my old self back. My priorities were askew, to say the least. And why did I accept without question that six weeks was this magical time frame that, when the clock strikes midnight a fairy godmother sprinkles some pixie dust, I would turn back into my prior self? Knowing what I know now, I can say with honesty that a regret of mine after the birth of my baby was not slowing down in life to really take the time to prioritize recovery and bonding with Matteo. *For as long I needed.* That should be what matters in the postpartum period.

Needless to say, after I recuperated from my back injury I realized that I no longer had a timeline to guide me on my recovery journey anymore. My six weeks had come and gone and I felt disoriented. My body was unrecognizable, I was sore everywhere, my joints ached, and my tailbone felt as though it was protruding six inches from my butt cheeks any time I tried to take a seat. My body did not feel like mine. I saw the importance of being physically healthy and finding a routine that I felt a sense of comfort in, but I was navigating uncharted territory. Where do I go from here?

Over the coming weeks, I began to listen to my body because I truly had no other option. Forget what *I thought* I knew about postpartum recovery and forget what my friends told me about their own experiences. I was putting more emphasis on what I believed I needed to live up to, instead of just *living*. Live as my body allowed, be self-aware, and just cut myself some slack!

So, when I finally shut down my expectations and asked my body what she needed, what was it that she told me?

- ***"Let me rest,"*** she said. "I am so tired," she said. "Have I not done enough for you? All I ask is for you to sleep when you can. Give me fuel so I can continue to heal." An important side note here: the voice I picture my body conveys is one of Beyoncé because my body is fierce and who is more powerful and all-mighty than Bey? And on an even more important note: believing I had a real conversation with my body either confirms that I was so sleep-deprived at the time I was on the verge of delirium, or somebody spiked my coffee with LSD that day.

Anyhow...

The importance of sleep is undeniably important. Sleeping supports the rejuvenation of our cells, helps us to recover from injuries, fight diseases, aids in the brainpower we need to make decisions and have conversations, and, well, any other function we perform on any given day. It's one of our most basic needs. There is no doubt about it, having a baby will disrupt your sleep, so this makes prioritizing rest even that much more essential. Studies show time and time again that sleep deprivation and mental health are closely linked; our resiliency seems to get misplaced when we don't get the rest our bodies need.[54] Since the loss of sleep is correlated to higher levels of anxiety and depression, finding ways to get some rest is vital to our well-being. As overused as the advice is, "sleep when the baby sleeps," it is truth to live by. It can feel overwhelming as a new mom to adjust to the schedule of your baby, feeling unsure about your abilities every step of the way, but newborns and their needs are quite simple: eat, poop, eat, poop, and sleep. They sleep a lot, especially in the beginning. So, guess what, that means you should be sleeping too. Put down the dishes, put down your phone, wave goodbye to your visitors, and nap whenever you can. If you can take a nap — just once in a while — you will be pleasantly surprised by how much better you will feel. Did you know that even a 30-minute catnap takes you into the restorative benefits that sleep provides?[55] Never underestimate the power of any nap that you can fit into your day.

One way we worked around some of the sleep deprivation that was occurring within our household was by Ryan and me sleeping in separate rooms. I moved into the spare bedroom, with Matteo's bassinet plunked beside my bed, while Ryan continued to sleep in the master. At first, it felt like a ginormous sacrifice of our marriage. Ryan and I always vowed we would put in the effort to maintain a healthy relationship and sleeping in separate rooms felt as though we were now just living as roommates. But while I was awoken every two hours by a crying baby who needed to fill his belly, it was beneficial to have Ryan sleep through the night because it made for a much more helpful partner throughout the day. Our thoughts were *at least* one of us needs to be rested because there is no benefit of us both being sleep deprived. And if we are both up at every feed throughout the night then nobody is getting rest. This was our way of sharing in the responsibility instead of equally drowning in it.

I promise you now that the sacrifice of Ryan and I giving up a few months of sleeping in the same bed ended up creating a closer bond for us because we knew we were looking out for each other. I have since migrated back to the master bedroom, when the timing was right for us; we caught up on all those nights apart and cuddle a little harder now.

Around the tenth week into our life as new parents, we felt as though we started to get a handle on a "schedule" (I use that word lightly because every time I thought we had a good thing going with Matteo's routine something would change all that). I would sneak away in the late evenings for a nap while Ryan spent some one-on-one time with Matteo. Sometimes it worked out to a full three hours of shut-eye before Ryan would gently wake me up to breastfeed, pass Matteo off, and then he would head to bed. This was a game-changer; having this rest time made me feel a little closer to normalcy. Even if Ryan went to bed earlier on some nights, knowing I could get a little snooze before the nightly feeding frenzy helped me immensely. Ryan thoroughly enjoyed this time to bond with our son, with the day obligations complete and a few hours of downtime before hitting the sack; he looked forward to this time every night. He would take his shirt off, tuck Matteo into his warm embrace for some skin-to-skin care and turn on a movie.

These strategies worked well for our family dynamic, though I know many others that would share in the responsibility throughout the night; one parent on call for the entire night shift, or scheduled feeds assigned to one or the other. As I mentioned earlier in chapter 6, my husband continually offered to be responsible for Matteo's night feeds, but I worried about my milk supply. I would have to get up to pump either way or I would wake up to leaking milk everywhere. On top of that, I knew the sound of my baby crying for the boob (no matter where he was in my house) would wake me long before my husband would crack open an eye. Then there was the hassle of Ryan getting the milk from the freezer, transferring to a bottle, and preparing it to just the right temperature before feeding Matteo. This seemed like too big of an ordeal for the middle of the night. To me, turning over in my bed to grab Matteo out of his bassinet and latch him in a matter of seconds just seemed like the right way to go about the night feeds. As always, there are endless suggestions and all that should matter to you is to take all the knowledge you come across and determine what works best for your family. Know that, though, no matter how you go about your routine, rest is an absolute must.

So, after having another LSD spiked coffee, what else did Beyoncé — I mean my body — tell me?

- **"I require some good bonding,"** she told me. "Bonding for our physical, emotional, and mental being is imperative. We are social creatures and the power of a little human touch is more beneficial than we may give it credit for."

The action of skin-to-skin, you may also have heard it be referred to as Kangaroo Care, is the actual physical connection of placing our unclothed baby on our bare chest. No barriers in the way, just their chest placed directly on ours. Your little one can be in a diaper, but needs nothing more than that and we should be shirtless. A receiving blanket may be placed over top for comfort and warmth. Remember it wasn't that long ago that little nugget of yours was a corporal part of your body, and when they are birthed there is a physical connection that is instantaneously severed. Though this isn't meant to be scary or unnatural — it is a process that is meant to happen — we can still ease into that extrauterine transition through skin-to-skin contact. Easing into the separation of one being becoming two through cuddles has been proven to benefit the mother-baby dyad. Though we may understand the warmth and comfort it provides on an emotional level, it's much more than that! Spending time in skin-to-skin regulates our baby's body temperature (our body temperature fluctuates to make sure our baby is not too hot and not too cold), regulates blood sugars, stabilizes their heart rate and breathing, can calm our baby, and decrease pain and crying. This is all done through the unbelievably powerful feeling of our baby and then releasing hormones that meet their needs.

But there's more! Skin-to-skin is also super beneficial for us. It promotes our physical healing and decreases our stress levels. Higher levels of skin-to-skin contact are linked to fewer incidences of postpartum depression and anxiety. Feeling a connection to baby shortly after giving birth can be a struggle for some new moms. You may look at this new human and they may feel like a stranger to you. It can be difficult to feel an automatic bond (sometimes not, but know that either feeling is normal) when you are learning how to care for them and what they need from you. It doesn't help, either, that newborns do not offer us validation; we don't hear "thank you, mommy," or "I love you, mommy," they don't smile or giggle, and sometimes we need those gestures as evidence we are doing a good job. Skin-to-skin can help create a bond that in other ways you may feel lacking. In doing so, it also promotes and supports breastfeeding — you didn't think there were even more benefits, did you? On top of being in a more ideal position to see and hear the cues of your soon-to-be hungry baby (in other words catching the early signs of hunger before they are screaming at you for their next meal), skin-to-skin contact causes a release in the hormone oxytocin, which is beneficial for our milk to flow more easily. This is all pretty amazing stuff if you ask me.

Now that we know how beneficial cuddling with our babies is, doesn't it make you want to embrace your little one right this second? If I could get my one-year-old to stop chasing our dog around my living room for just a moment, I would love to take a break from writing this chapter and curl Matteo right up into my chest. So let it be heard, you can never cuddle your baby too much. No matter what you are told by your friends and family, cuddle your baby as much as you desire. If they want to tell you otherwise, let them know that as you lay there on the couch you are actually taking the time to regulate your baby's blood sugar levels. See what they have to say about that for productivity in your downtime. Even as your baby continues to grow and become more independent, the bonding, comfort, and trust built between you and your little one are always strengthened during an embrace, so have at it! Mother-to-baby connection is a physiologic process backed by science and should play a big part in our parenting role.

It's important to mention that if you are a trauma survivor skin-to-skin can sometimes feel overwhelming. There can be times the position of your baby, the nakedness, or the sensation could lead to a negative trigger, so be cognizant if you fall into this category.[56] Also know that it's always okay to feel the need to take a break from cuddles when you need some time to yourself.

Which brings me to the importance of daddy's cuddles.

The bonding for any other parent and their baby through skin-to-skin is very beneficial. After my Caesarean section, I was able to witness from the operating room table my husband skin-to-skin with Matteo and the joy on my husband's face during that moment was unforgettable. Remember, there are many responsibilities as the birthing parent that we cannot pass off to someone else, which sometimes makes our significant others feel inadequate. When they can embrace their baby skin-to-skin, they take on the responsibility of protection, warmth, comfort, and bonding that they deserve to experience.

Skin-to-skin is considered a separate experience from sleeping, so when we offer our partner this responsibility, that gives us the time to close our eyes and get some rest. When you are ready to get some shut-eye, let your partner have a turn with some cuddles and interaction. Though I know others may not agree (and here I will bring out my nursing voice), skin-to-skin is a time to bond, not to sleep. This is for everyone's safety. We have likely never experienced the level of sleep deprivation that mothers with a new baby experience. So, as new mothers, we cannot truly be confident in our capabilities when we do fall asleep. As comforting as it is to have your baby on your chest, we have seen one too many babies' safety compromised when a parent falls asleep in this position. If it is a physiological reason to have your newborn on your chest (meaning they need you to regulate their heart rate, blood sugar, etc.) and you cannot manage to stay awake any longer, then it should be the duty of your partner to supervise skin-to-skin while you doze off. Alternative strategies that support you to stay awake while providing skin-to-skin care: chew gum, drink some ice water, have a snack, Facetime, or call the funniest person you know to keep you entertained.

Still on the topic of cuddling, let's move now to the importance of an embrace between you and your significant other. Even though every ounce of your being is given to your baby, it does not take any more energy to cuddle your partner for a few minutes. While no energy is exerted in a hugging embrace, you may be pleasantly surprised by the energy you may gain from such an interaction. I remember my sister telling me that four months after having her son, she laid with her husband for a quick spoon session (really just a spoon nothing more!) and the warmth and touch of her husband's embrace made her bawl uncontrollably. She said she didn't realize until that moment how much she was craving to reconnect with him and the power of that hug for just a few moments brought them back to the feeling of caring for one another.

We all know how much friends and family, coworkers, neighbours, cousins want to hold your new baby. I get it. Our babies are just too dang cute for anyone to resist a good cuddle sesh. I have been there and I have also been that annoying friend-with-baby-fever that just needed all the new baby cuddles I could get; ignorant to how the mom felt about me taking bonding time away from them. But this really shouldn't be something any mother needs to feel. I hear it so often from mothers with a new baby: this unwritten rule to be a hostess to a constant stream of guests the second after delivery. Don't get me wrong, if you feel as though you are ready to enjoy some company and a little celebration, then relish in that time. *But* if you have countless amounts of visitors in and out of your home, then I hope at least one of them vacuumed a room or two for you or folded your laundry. I sure hope someone brought you over some food, instead of you serving them as they take your precious cuddles away. If you are feeling overwhelmed with your baby in your arms hour after hour, they've been changed, fed, and happy, then having those visitors there for some respite for you is warranted *if that's what you as their mother decide.* If you feel as though you are watching the clock and allowing someone to embrace your newborn just to appease them, well I want to tell you: you don't have to let this happen!

My sister-in-law once told me, "everyone that came over

wanted to cuddle my baby when I didn't need help in that department. *I* wanted to cuddle my baby because it was a special bonding time for us, and that was what I felt my baby needed. What I needed help with was in every other department." So I say, how about you grab the broom over there and get to work and I will continue to cuddle my baby thank you very much!

Let's ask our guests to **grab the broom, not our babies** to remind everyone that it's time to bring back the community needed to raise a newborn. The right way to support a new mother is to worry about her needs as she worries about her baby's. If you are unsure what a new mom needs help with then ask yourself this: if I spent every 24 hours in a day focused solely on keeping a completely vulnerable, dependent, and defenseless human alive, what would I not have time to do? The answer: everything else! Cooking, cleaning, laundry, walking the dog, emptying the cat litter box, picking up groceries, making the bed, cleaning up spit-up on every blanket, shirt, and couch cushion I own... I can continue if you haven't caught my drift just yet.

There needs to be a community mentality within the support systems of our young families that are in those childrearing years; it really does take a village, remember chapter 12? Supporting a new mom to help her meet her needs means we are focusing on strengthening her well-being and in doing so helps our entire future generation grow up in the healthiest, most loving, and supportive environments.

- **"Give me nourishment,"** was my body's third plea.

Healthy nourishing food. Though this is important all the time, it's imperative while we are healing and supporting another human being. Drink about three litres of water each day and eat roughly 500 more calories per day when you are breastfeeding through healthy snacks and meals of protein, good fats, vitamins, and minerals.[57] This is also not the time to ever worry about decreasing caloric intake for weight loss. Do I need to repeat myself here? This is not the time to worry about decreasing caloric intake for weight loss! This is a time to be healthy and fuel your body. Period. But I know what you are thinking because I am thinking it too. When you have a new baby how the hell are you supposed to whip up chef-grade, nutrient-dense, fresh food?

You're not.

I truly believe this expectation doesn't make any sense whatsoever for a mother who has just delivered a baby. She needs to heal, rest, and bond with her child. And this is, once again, where we need help. Do I sound like a broken record yet?

One of my favourite gifts we received after delivering Matteo was from Ryan's Fire Station. His crew pitched on a large sum toward a Skip-the-Dishes gift card. The number of times that gift card saved us from cooking (and, even more, the cleanup of cooking) was the most practical gift for two young adults trying to navigate parenthood. And, welcome to the 21st century, we have come so far from the days of only pizza or donair doorstep delivery. We had limitless healthy meal options for delivery at any time of the day.

There are also loads of options for meal trains, which is a fancy term for friends and family to slot themselves into a schedule and provide you with a meal. They can just drop it at your front door and, voila, your dinner is ready to be served! I hope, though, this is an understanding that meal trains are to help the family with food and are not considered extra visits for baby cuddles, capiche? It doesn't take much for someone to make you a meal or two for the grief and energy it saves you, and I can tell you from experience those simple gestures are life-changing. Not to mention, it's the same amount of money spent on groceries in its place of those extra baby clothes, or blankets they would have purchased as a gift instead. Websites that support meal train setup even offer you the ability to input dietary restrictions, allergies, and suggestions, so you are gifted meals that work best for your family. Utilizing such websites is a great option, but realistically any meal train can be set up as simply as through a group text or email chain.

Meal prepping frozen meals before you deliver is always a smart idea so that your biggest effort toward cooking on any day is merely pulling it out of the freezer and throwing it in your oven. Oh, the hours and effort you could save in a day! Other options for healthy meals are meal prep services that are delivered to your front door. You are provided all the ingredients, pre-portioned for the dish, with simple instructions on how to prepare it. These can be costly, though, so it's not for everyone. I use a curbside pick-up grocery service that doesn't cost any more money for my groceries to be picked, bagged, and loaded into my car after I put through my list online.

- **"Last, but not least, I need some movement in my life,"** my body told me. Let me explain this one before the LSD wears off.

A little movement each day has a positive impact on our physical, mental, emotional, and spiritual bodies. I don't want to scare you off preaching the need for exercise, though, because it's not as frightening as it sounds. If you feel the need to run a marathon or take a CrossFit class, then the next few pages may not be worth your time. But if you do not fall into the extreme-sports-after-delivering-a-baby category, well then as long as you are getting up and moving each day, I am happy. When I pulled my back out trying to jump back into my old workout routine six weeks after having Matteo, I still prioritized some form of movement each day because I knew how important it was for my sanity.

So how can you incorporate enough movement in a day that makes you feel good mentally and physically? My baby carrier was one of the best purchases for me. Stuffing Matteo into this apparatus was comforting for both of us. It allowed me the freedom to get moving, even during his naps times as he would just fall asleep on my chest, and I had two hands free so I could enjoy a warm beverage without feeling like I was a juggling circus animal. I was able to use my carrier in all seasons, on the hottest of summer days or even in the dead of winter we bundled up in snowsuits and got outside. When my body was ready I did Baby Barre with him strapped to me, walked hills by my house, or even on those rainy days I would load him into my carrier and to the basement we went to walk on the treadmill.

I also enrolled us in Mom-and-Baby Yoga and sometimes we did yoga together in the comfort of our living room — meaning Matteo would lie underneath me and giggled as I tried to bend like a pretzel around him. Other days my movement consisted of nothing more than just stretching my body out.

Get moving, that's all there is to it.

Don't stress about shedding that baby weight; move to feel good, and get some blood flowing to support your healing. If you think you need to work out and jump on your scale ten times a day only to be disappointed at your results, that's not what is going to keep your motivation up and, yes, I was one of those people that stepped on the scale ten times a day, so I get it! Move for your mental health. Do it for your well-being. Pay attention to how much better you feel physically, emotionally, mentally, and spiritually — you are on the right track to living a healthier life. And the bonus: if you are doing it for mental health and find consistency in your routine, the baby weight *will* come off.

Now let's talk sex. (Don't worry, Mom, I will keep this PG.) What other better movement than reconnecting with your significant other? When it comes to getting back under the sheets after delivering a baby, some of us are ready much earlier and others are ready much later. Do not feel obligated to get back to it once that fairy godmother sprinkles that pixie dust on your six-week mark if you do not feel ready physically or, just as important, emotionally. On the flip side, don't feel you need to hold back if you are ready before that. Have a conversation with your doctor and ask for an individualized assessment to make sure you are healed at any stage, and get excited to get back under those sheets as soon as you feel ready.

Interestingly, proper movement in a day has the power to increase your energy levels, so push yourself to do a little exercise — whatever that means to you — without those high expectations we put on ourselves for the wrong reasons.

In chapter 12 we delved into the importance of prioritizing your life. And we all know life's priorities can seem a little overwhelming most days. Since becoming a mom, I have revamped my workout routine to a mere 30 minutes. As much as I know a hardcore, hour-long run-'til-you puke workout would make me feel like a boss, I get overwhelmed that this will soak up all my free time in a day. Though exercise is important to me it's not *everything*. Finding a balance meant decreasing my routine to a dedicated 30 minutes, which made me happy for getting in my movement, but even more happy that I still had time left to do other things, like wash my hair because that doesn't get done nearly enough these days.

Throughout this chapter our bodies were discussed as a

separate entity; there is a reason for this. Think of the advice you would give your best friend if she said she was struggling to lose the baby weight, struggling to breastfeed, struggling to find the time to eat healthy, and on top of it all, feeling severely sleep-deprived. You would likely feel a deep compassion for her and you would offer her support, am I right? Would you have such high expectations that you tell her to just push through and figure it out, even as she is reaching out and genuinely opening up about her struggles? I would guess you wouldn't. You would tell her to prioritize rest, ask for help, and to screw all those responsibilities in life that aren't so important right now and aren't aiding in her healing and well-being.

Now take a second to think of how hard we are on ourselves. The expectations we have to just figure it all out and do it all. Working extra hard to care for our babies, making food, cleaning our houses during a time we need to be resting, recovering, and simply bonding with our little ones. We've talked a lot about self-love but don't forget about *self-compassion*. If we detach from our bodies and treat them as a separate vessel — distinct from our minds for just a second — I believe we can appreciate our physical body for everything she is and respect the recovery she deserves. In turn, appreciating the physical processes of everything we are capable of will give us a healthier sense of well-being.

Now drop and give me 20!

Just kidding :)

14
CHILL OUT

How to Pull Yourself out of Unproductive Anxiety

LET'S warm up this chapter with a challenge:

A CHALLENGE FOR YOU

Set an alarm for a couple of random times throughout the day. When your alarm goes off, no matter where you are, take a few moments to stop and reflect on what you are doing and how you are feeling. Now focus on your breath. Is it short and shallow because you are trying to finish a deadline at work? Are you in the middle of supper and laughing as your little one is trying hard to manoeuver a piece of watermelon into their mouth? Take the time to see if your feelings and your actions are related to stress or if you are calm and relaxed. If you are noticing some tension, close your eyes and take five deep, refreshing, and resetting breaths before you continue on your day. With each breath count to four as you fill your lungs all the way to full capacity and then four again as you completely exhale your breath all the way out. The point of this exercise is to ground us back to a calm state by simply being cognizant of our feelings and using our breath to reset ourselves.

Learning to focus on your breath is a small, simple preparation for many anxiety-reducing strategies we can put in our toolbox. Our breath is the foundation of these strategies and it's also the very foundation of life. Never underestimate the power of breathing. It is truly the only thing that stays with you from your birth until your death. Everything else could change – your hair colour, your friends, your job – but the ever-existing constant is your breath.[58] Even more, breath is a symptom of every emotion. Just as within the challenge at the start of this chapter, if you take the time to focus on your breath, you may notice a change in its depth and pattern as you feel different emotions. When you stub your toe your breath speeds up as you fight through the pain. If you are angry, you may take deeper breaths and, even in delight, you may witness a lighter breath. Therefore, if we can "[learn] to navigate and manage [our] breath [we are being taught] to navigate any situation in life."[59]

Breathing is an important piece of your wellness because it is with you wherever you are. Being connected to your breath at all times makes this a very accessible strategy. A strategy that will support you to gain back control when being consumed by feelings of panic or anxiety.

So many strategies throughout the chapters in this book are focused on an upstream approach to our mental health and well-being. In other words, we are gaining resiliency through strategies to feel better supported so that we can be the warrior mothers we know we are and halt those feelings of worry, angst, stress, and depression before they even begin. Those strategies are in place to act as our armour and *keep* us healthy. But what happens when, no matter what we do to sustain our shielding armour, we are caught in a moment and find ourselves panicked by our thoughts, debilitated by our feelings, or dealing with a situation that puts us in an unhealthy mind space? When we do begin to feel these things, it's time to *fix* the problem. So, let's learn a strategy to work through those feelings at that moment in time they are happening.

THE C.H.I.L.L. O.U.T. STRATEGY

As mentioned in the very first chapter of this book, the purpose of anxiety is to help us recognize threats and follow through on decisions to keep us safe. Though this is imperative for our survival, it can also bring us into a heightened fear-based emotional state that can be hard as hell to get out of. When we become debilitated by our feelings, anxiety is no longer productive.

Let's picture anxiety as our opponent in the game of motherhood. It is constantly challenging us and causing us to question our ability. It may hinder us from doing all the things we thought we were capable of or it may bring in fears that cause us to struggle through overwhelming days and restless nights. Anxiety may also cause rifts within our relationships, especially if others can't understand the worries we feel faced with. But, as within any healthy competition in life, being victorious over our opponent signifies that we can come out the other side as a better competitor. If we can gain the skillset to overcome the feelings of unproductive anxiety, we will become improved, more resilient versions of our strong selves. This is how we are going to triumph over our fierce challenger in just three steps.

STEP 1: INTERFERENCE

In this first step, the focus is on pulling yourself out of your anxious thoughts. I am sure most, if not all, of us walking this planet have been faced with a seed of a thought that forces us to either cut that thought at the root or water it and let it grow. When we are growing a weed – a bad thought – we must cut it at the root. Giving anxious thoughts our attention can cause them to run wild on us; consequently, as our opponent strikes, we must block it from entering into our zone. The goal here is to de-escalate from the heightened state we find ourselves in when that threat we believe is there is not, in fact, real. Some simple and common suggestions for pulling yourself out of these thoughts:

- *Change of Scenery:* can you remove yourself from the current situation that is bringing up feelings of anxiety? Sometimes this little change can give you the space you need to breathe.
- *Change of Temperature*: research suggests that feeling a drastic temperature change can help essentially "snap you out of" anxiety. While it doesn't sounds too comforting, it has been suggested that dunking your head in cold water can quickly drop your blood pressure, which in turn drops the emotional intensity you are feeling. An easier way to get these feelings, rather than sticking your head in a bucket of ice, would be to run your fingers under cold water, hold ice cubes in your hand, or place an ice pack on the back of your neck. Keep in mind, this change of temperature is meant to be quick and isn't needed for more than a mere few seconds

to a couple of minutes. On the flip side, a warmer temperature exposure can also be beneficial, such as a warm shower to relax your muscles, which destresses your body and, in turn, can destress your mind. Warmth can be more beneficial for depressive symptoms, as the heart rate in these emotions tend to be lower, and hot will make the change in your body by increasing it.

- *Five, Four, Three, Two, One:* this is one of my favourite strategies, taught to me by one of our family therapists. I love it because it's so simple, easy to remember, and can be done anywhere at any time. When feeling overwhelmed take a moment to pause and focus on your immediate surroundings. Find five things that you can see, four things you can touch, three things you can hear, two things you can smell, and one thing you can taste. As you seek them out say the objects out loud and by the time you get down to "one," I promise you will feel a little more grounded.
- *Utilize your Support System:* distract yourself with those around you who can help you do just that. Have a few people on speed-dial you know you can trust to help when you feel panic or anxiety coming on. The people you choose should understand their role when you feel the need to reach out to them. I find it helpful to FaceTime my sister, knowing my niece and nephew can always put a smile on my face, or call my mom who knows me better than I know myself. I also find a lot of comfort in reaching out to my mom-friends who are in the trenches with me, such as texting my Wine O'clock Crew group chat. There often isn't a situation another mom finds completely absurd or can't relate to; it's always comforting knowing you are reaching out to someone who understands what you are going through.

- *Distraction Activities*: the list of distraction activities you could partake in is endless, but your list should be completely personal. The idea here is to find fun, lighthearted actions that allow you to change your focus from panic. Be mindful of what you feel will be a healthy way to interfere your thoughts. For a reminder on healthy influences scroll back through chapter 11. Try blaring a few of your favourite songs, look through a picture album, have a five-minute dance party with your baby, or listen to an uplifting podcast. You may not find checking your emails, for instance, a healthy distraction because you cannot control what is waiting for you in your inbox and may only add to your anxiety. Your techniques need to be a guarantee, with no chance for further anxiety or stress to be built upon.

Being a mother, it can be difficult to focus on yourself when there is a baby strapped to you all day. Many of the distraction suggestions listed above are simple and accessible to do when you are with your little one. It is important to put this strategy to use no matter where you are or what you are doing when you begin to feel anxious. However, there are times when the power of anxiety makes the situation you are in feel unsafe to the point that you may need to put your child down somewhere for the time being. This will allow you the focus to work through your feelings. Maybe you need to place them in a safe space like their crib or playpen for ten minutes. Maybe someone else is around that could watch your baby while you concentrate on yourself. Though this may feel unnatural, it's important for the safety of you and your child to always have a safe space available when necessary.

STEP 2: CHALLENGE

Back to the competition with our ever-so tenacious opponent, anxiety. What's the next step after we have defended our competitor from entering our zone? We have distracted those thoughts that were bringing us into the realm of unproductivity and now we need to endure to get us back to our healthy selves. If the first step is our defense, our second step is going to bring us into a position of offense.

To do so, we are going to fight back against those anxious thoughts that we are falling victim to and challenge them with logic. Anxiety is not truth. Far-fetched or not, anxiety could be the fear of possibilities, fear of what is to come, or fear of a particular outcome. It is not, though, the actuality of the present or the future. We need to talk to ourselves with logical points to bring us back into the true reality of our existence.

There are two reasons for this step. Firstly, we are teaching ourselves to be present in the moment, instead of falling victim to the truth anxiety wants us to believe. Think back to chapter 10 when I locked Matteo in the car. I was terrified, but he was okay. My mind went to every worst-case scenario surrounding the safety of my child. But the true reality of the situation was, for all he knew, he was just chillin' in his car seat like any other time. He was safe, he wasn't overheating, he wasn't hungry, he wasn't locked in there forever, he didn't get glass in his eye from me punching my fist through the side window and shattering it all over his precious face. All of these possibilities went through my mind, yes, but none of them were the facts of the current situation. **It's important to ask yourself if the thoughts that are in your mind are facts**.

The second reason we talk logic is to validate ourselves as mothers and boost our confidence, even just a little. Just as we discussed when counting our blessings, if we look for gratitude, we will find it. Well, here, I want you to look for truth and, as always, when you look for it, it will be discovered. No doubt, this can be a tough step because an overwhelming surge of anxiety rids our mind of logic. It may make perfect sense to look for logic when you are feeling great, but anxiety can take you into a mind space that is far from reasonable. Practice looking inward to search for your strengths, your special qualities, and all your capabilities. When you seek them out, shout it from the rooftops.

Confidence in oneself will help counteract the uncertainty and fear bred by panic and anxiety. You *are* an amazing mom. You *are* doing things right. Every time you look at those perfectly round chubby cheeks and blue eyes know that your baby is happy, healthy, and you *are* meeting all their needs. Yes, you are. Remember that. Let's try to wire our brains to focus on the things we are doing well and, I promise you, there are a lot of things on that list. Don't underestimate every action you do in a day for your baby: every diaper change, every kiss, and every song you sing. If we constantly focus on the negatives or the screw-ups, like accidentally catching their skin when clipping their nails, then that negative outlook becomes our reality. I know for a fact that every little screw-up you think you have done, like clipping their skin, is followed by an army of good actions you could use to swallow up the bad and spit it out.

STEP 3: RECOVERY

We have played interference on our anxious thoughts, and we have challenged their truth. We've been on the defense and then pushed back on offense. When we come to the end of the battle, what's the next step? Recovery, of course! If you have ever run a marathon, played a game of soccer, or gone to the gym, then you know how important recovery is. Any athlete out there knows that to be successful proper rest and recovery are crucial. If we understand this physically, then we need to understand the importance of mental recovery just the same.

When we reach step three, it's time to repair the angst our mind, body, and spirit have gone through. Taking proper care of ourselves will help us recover from the stress we have been through, while simultaneously elevating our resiliency for future meltdowns.

After a rough day of feeling consumed by anxious thoughts, sometimes I push my unfolded laundry to the side and do some yoga in my basement instead. Other days it simply means I am packing Matteo up in the car to drive to my local café, relax with my favourite warm beverage and take a little mental health break. We have talked a lot about self-care, but if you need a reminder or some inspiration, turn back to chapter 6.

You may find a slight overlap between your recovery and your interference methods. For instance, dancing could be a great distraction, while also something that you do for your self-care. Just remind yourself **step one is to change your immediate thoughts, step three is to foster your resiliency and build up your armour.**

So how, you may ask, with these three steps are we CHILLin' OUT?

C: commit to

H: healing by causing

I: interference on those anxious thoughts. Use

L: logic and

L: love for yourself to

O: oppose anxious ideas and then

U: unwind with

T: therapeutic exercises.

Learning how to incorporate the C.H.I.L.L. O.U.T. strategy in your life will give you one more tool to calm your anxiety when you feel as though you are being swept up in it. Putting this method into practice is proving your ***commitment to healing*** as you learn and implement important strategies for your mental health and well-being. Becoming an expert in these strategies, taking the initiative to feel better, and promising yourself you will take care of this. You must cause ***interference*** on those nasty thoughts of anxiety, breaking up that black cloud that's blocking your sunshine. Distract yourself and use healthy strategies to bring you back to reality instead of getting captured by the fabricated future in your mind. Using ***logic and love*** for yourself ***oppose*** your thoughts by speaking the truth about the situation. Ground yourself in the true realities of the present (facts versus fiction) and speak to yourself about the control you do have and how powerful you are as a mom. Find anything in you to prove to yourself that you are better than your thoughts. This is not just a superficial idea; this is you speaking truth to yourself. Change that mindset. Remind yourself you are a great mom and that you are more powerful than anxiety is giving you credit for. When all of this is done take the time to ***unwind*** using ***therapeutic exercises.*** Unwind physically and emotionally; you need to recover holistically. And here we cue our self-care measures. After doing all of these important steps to counteract anxiety we have begun to ***CHILL OUT***.

Anxiety means different things to different people and, as we talked about earlier on in this book, can look and feel distinct to everyone, which means we may all need our own ways of coping. I don't claim to be a doctor or a healer, but I can tell you this: every strategy and every skill we can keep in our back pocket will help us become stronger and more resilient than we were the day before. You must learn to utilize the strategies that work for you, whatever that may be. If the strategies you use are healthy options, then you can be confident that it's helping you to heal.

ALLOW YOURSELF TO FEEL ALL THE FEELS

-Nikki P.
Mom to Abbey

15
WHEN THINGS AREN'T AS YOU HAD HOPED

Dealing with Unexpected Challenges

I want to open this very important chapter with a shout-out to an amazing girlfriend of mine who was my inspiration for this topic. It was crucial to include a chapter about dealing with unexpected challenges in a book about maternal mental health; we cannot always say everything is going to be okay when maybe something is truly not okay. It should come as no surprise that postpartum depression and anxiety can be triggered when you are faced with unanticipated hardships with your child because this can lead to providing extra care, fearing what the future holds, making life-altering decisions, dealing with emotional strain, and so much more.

My friend, Nikki, is candid, authentic, and willing to open up about exactly that. Her beautiful boy, Abbey, was born with a condition called hip dysplasia. One day I casually asked her the same question I ask all my new mom friends: *If you could give advice to all the new moms out there, knowing what you know now, what would it be?* Here is what she said:

"I would tell new moms that no matter what, it's okay to feel any feeling you have. And no book or person should tell you to feel differently. If you're sad, be sad and if you're happy, be happy — no matter how small the win. And feel everything in between! I was very emotional and low about having a baby with a condition. I was told...that it was my fault and I need to toughen up and be strong for the baby. I was told I can't sulk in the fact that I didn't have a perfectly healthy baby like I dreamed I would.

I was scared of all the things they would do to him at the hospital and sad for the fact that I couldn't change the situation for my perfect little human. You eventually get more educated... and the more you learn, the stronger you get and the better you feel. But some days are shit and the hospital would give me bad news and the only thing that would keep me sane was having a good, long, ugly cry and talking to my husband. I realized it was totally okay to feel sorry for myself, and for my baby, and the things he had to go through so young.

Initially, I felt guilty because... it could have been a lot worse. Yet, hormones amplified my emotions and made me feel as though my situation was the worst out there. So, as a new mom, I allowed myself to feel all the feels and to express it how I felt was best for me."

I hope that hearing from a mother who has lived through hours of therapy, endless education, hospital visits, emotional turmoil stemming from her son's diagnosis will help you feel a little less isolated. Understand, just as Nikki explained, there will be many emotions you feel throughout your journey. Feel them and, just as we learned in chapter 11, healthily work through them to spark positive change.

THE MOST SPECIAL OUTCOMES

As the Educator on a postpartum unit, I thoroughly enjoy setting up Lunch and Learns for our staff. During the nurses' lunch break, they are invited to a 30-minute presentation on a specific topic that we feel would be beneficial for them to learn more about. There was one session in particular that stuck with me. A couple of years ago we collaborated with the Canadian Down Syndrome Society and had mothers open up to us about raising a child diagnosed with Down syndrome. This was one of the most inspirational days of my life. I have never learned so much as I did that particular day, and the most important takeaway for me: **the biggest challenges can lead to the most special outcomes.** All the mothers who told their story gleamed with pride about how exceptional their child was; they were so smart, so thoughtful, so loving, so full of life, and they brought so much more meaning to their parents' world than they had ever felt before.

Many new parents are terrified of the challenges they may be faced with, but when I say that every child is a blessing and what we can learn from each one of them is immense, I mean this wholeheartedly. Sharing other people's experiences adds so much value to the education I offer in these pages because even though I have been through my share of hardships, there are others that have been through so much more. I want this book to help *all* mothers out there, no matter what their journey.

You may be a mother that had a scare at an ultrasound, predicting an anomaly in your fetus. Maybe you have been through a

Neonatal Intensive Care Unit admission with your little one, or are in the midst of life-changing heart surgery on a baby that is only months old. Maybe your child was born with hip dysplasia or Down syndrome. If you are someone who is going through a particular struggle – whatever that may be – and having a difficult time navigating life, the first step I ask of you is to learn as much as you can and find a community that will support you in your journey. There are specialized therapists, societies, and support groups for almost anything on the planet. There are also other families going through a similar struggle to what you are faced with, I promise you that. Begin by asking your Public Health Nurse, your family doctor, a specialist if you have already been referred to one, your friends or family, or use the internet to find out what resources are out there. This important first step will provide you with the support that you need, with people in your corner that you can truly empathize with, and you will learn more than you ever could if you were to go through this alone.

THE WILLINGNESS TO LEARN

In my experience with Ryan's PTSD diagnosis, there was a point in my journey I felt the need to find a therapist of my own, separate from the therapy we were doing for him. I needed help to determine and understand *my role* in all of it. There were the challenges of the diagnosis we were learning how to manage, but I was also going through my own separate struggles, as a wife dealing with a husband with a condition. So, I ask you, would your own therapy (for your own healing) be beneficial?

Remember: *we don't know what we don't know,* so learn all you can from as many different perspectives. Knowledge can be so powerful, especially when dealing with unknown territory. Anxiety and fear of the future can be exacerbated if we feel ill-equipped for unanticipated hardships. Having the willingness to learn will give you the strength to face your challenges head-on. Even if you may not have a particular struggle at this moment, think about how empowering it could be to take an infant CPR class, for example. Having the skills to perform basic life support or to intervene on a choking baby could provide you a level of confidence you may not have had before; that preparedness will better protect your mental health. Never stop learning.

Some other actions that may help you if you are going through a particular challenge:

- *Express your emotions to the healthcare staff/your support system and they will educate you.*
- *Ask lots of questions.*
- *Keep a journal of the journey.* Not only will this help you be reminded of all that you have learned along the way, but it can also be used as a therapeutic outlet.
- *While being respectful of others' opinions, such as family members, practice saying no unapologetically, even if they push their opinions and judgements onto you after you have made your decision.* This is a tough one, but choosing to do what is best for your baby needs to take priority over their feelings (see chapter 9).
- *Take some space from those who are not supporting you in a way you feel you need to be supported* (see chapter 11).
- *Trust yourself to make decisions for your family.*
- *Make time for self-care.* The term respite means you are asking for help for you to recharge and be the best caregiver

you can. You may need some support from those around you to help take care of you, your baby, the dishes in the sink, or the laundry piling up in the corner (see chapter 6).

BIRTH TRAUMA

There are countless challenges we may be faced with as we raise our children and what we have discussed prior are only a few small examples. Experiencing any type of trauma during the birth of your child is another massive trigger to postpartum depression or anxiety diagnoses. You may feel this is a category you fall into, regardless of the outcome of the birth, meaning you don't need to experience something *bad* to warrant feelings of trauma. It is proven that the most important predictor of PTSD is a negative subjective experience of the individual; meaning if she believes the experience to be life-threatening, endangering, or bad, then that is her truth, even if others involved see it as a routine birth.[60] A good friend of mine who delivered a healthy baby boy via a Caesarean section was devastated by her birthing journey. She truly believed unequivocally that she was capable of delivering vaginally and when she didn't, it sent her into a spiral of negative self-thoughts and depression. She had constant flashbacks of the experience in which feelings of loss of control and pain were overwhelming, even though there were no adverse outcomes for her or her newborn. Even so, she constantly thought about the experience which she felt that she lost out on — what she had hoped for — and couldn't understand why she was unable to deliver her baby on her own.

A CHALLENGE FOR YOU

If you are struggling with trauma from your birthing journey, write it out. Write it out as soon as you recognize you are haunted from one part or another and while it's fresh in your mind. Write what happened, how you felt, and what surprised you. Tuck it away somewhere and come back to it in six weeks. How do you feel about your journey now? Is it still something that haunts you? Do you still carry strong feelings of regret or feelings of being out of control? Do you still feel the need to heal from your experience? Re-write your experience to see if you now carry a different recollection of events, in a more positive light. Maybe you look at your beautiful baby who is growing and learning and you have come to realize that everything happened just as it should.

Though I would love to write a book to each person individually as to what they need to overcome their struggles or the trauma they suffered, our journeys are too unique for this to be possible. That said, I promise there are options for you if you feel the need to heal mentally, physically, or emotionally from your birthing experience. There are counsellors out there, healers, doctors, and therapists. You may have friends who could listen to your story and cry with you if that's what you feel you need. Having the ability to just talk it out sometimes can be beneficial for your healing. There are also strategies such as meditation, mindfulness, journaling, exposure therapy, and other therapy, such as cognitive behavioural therapy and EMDR, which are very effective to overcome trauma. Sometimes merely time is all that is needed to heal your wounds.

Let's go back to counting our blessings just one more time because changing our perspective is too important for our mental health for us to forget. I want you to practice this as much as possible, in as many different situations as possible. So here we go, can you find three blessings in your birthing story that make you a little more grateful for your experience? Was your significant other by your side the entire time? That can be remarkable to feel that sense of teamwork during such an exponential moment in your life. It could have been your midwife who was extra calming during the hardest points in the birth of your child or maybe it was just one particular nurse that made everything so much better. It could have been a certain intervention, such as an epidural, that allowed you to focus that much more to get that baby out of you. I will, once again, share with you my three blessings as some inspiration as you think of yours:

1. As soon as I was stitched up from my c-section and rolled into the recovery room, my nurse latched Matteo to my breast without skipping a beat and he breastfed like a champ. I am so grateful for the nurse that assisted in making this happen so seamlessly.
2. Though Matteo was wedged inside of me for what felt like forever, we were able to constantly monitor his heart rate and he was never under dire distress through the birthing process.
3. Not only did I have the most fabulous team in the hospital taking care of Matteo and me, but my husband also called our prenatal instructor during my active labour and she gave us tips and tricks to get Matteo in an ideal position for delivery. Though I still ended up needing a c-section, I couldn't believe how many people I had in my corner cheering me on.

GROWING THROUGH HARDSHIPS

There is an entire 40 weeks of pregnancy that could be filled with unexpected hardships; there are also countless stories that are out of our control the first year of motherhood, and every year of motherhood following. We need to find ways to perceive our journey as experiences that help us grow and find the meaning within the pages of our stories.

I remember speaking to my therapist after experiencing a miscarriage and I said to her, "I just really don't want this to forever change the person I am."

Her response: "But every situation we go through changes us. We are always evolving as humans, so yes, it is going to change you and we need to find a way for you to see the value in that."

Those words changed my perspective drastically. Before I truly felt that I was this person, in the here and now and that is exactly who I want to continue to be until my dying days. With just those thoughts alone, I realized how fearful I was of change and how ignorant I was to my personal growth. Now when faced with challenges there is a fire lit inside me that gets me motivated to see how I'll be able to persevere and the new me that evolves on the other side. Evolution is important to our existence; it's exhilarating and we can only evolve when we unreservedly live life. Live life by embracing challenges, problem-solving, and overcoming adversity in healthy ways to help us grow as individuals as well as mothers, friends, sisters, and wives. Living life does not mean having an existence that steers us clear of pain and fear or trials and tribulations. We are not in control of what difficulties we will be faced with, but we are responsible for how we live through it. We are responsible for how we choose to interpret these events in our lives.

As much as we think seeking out a life of no problems is what we need to strive for, the most struggling times can be the most meaningful experiences. Let's get it straight people**, there is no such thing as a life without challenges!** What we can do though is expect that life comes with problems and take those on as warriors rather than as victims. Seek out the blessings, find the meaning, and look for the growth and the strength that enters your life.

Mark Manson is a well-known American author who wrote the book *The Subtle Art of Not Giving a F*ck*. In there he speaks to the idea that human instinct is to face problems and overcome them, not live a problem-free life. It can make us happier individuals to encounter a problem, overcome it, and gain gratitude for what we have in this special life than to have no problems at all. Think about this for a second: **we can improve our overall happiness to have challenges in life that we endure.** This means we work through our struggles and when we do, our perspective of our life can be a positive one. It may not seem so at the time, but when we look back at our life challenges and pat ourselves on the back for coming out the other side, we can become happier, more appreciative individuals. That is the perception we as new moms need to create in our minds.

When we feel victim to our situations or the problems we have been handed, then happiness will not flourish through such a mentality. Feeling victim means we feel hopeless, out of control, and cheated in some way that we did not deserve. Survivors feel resiliency, a sense of achievement, and triumph. What outlook do you want to have? I am here to remind you, once again, how blessed motherhood is. How blessed we are for having these little nuggets in our lives. And while we will teach them their ABCs and how to say "please and thank you", they will always be teaching us so much more.

A LETTER TO MATTEO

One day my sister and I were chatting about motherhood when she asked me if I had ever written a letter to my son. As new moms, we have so many emotions and writing can be a way to sort through them. It can help to delve into what you are feeling and find sense within them. It can also be extremely therapeutic to reminisce about the wonderful memories created since having your baby.

So that is exactly what I did.

It was the night before Matteo's first birthday and I decided to write him a letter and put it in his birthday card. My idea was to stash it away in his baby book for him to read one day. Maybe he will read it on his 18th birthday, when he moves out of the house, or maybe when he is ready to have children of his own. **I wanted this letter to be filled with the memories of this very special time — the first year of our lives together — before they get lost in the busyness of our life to come.** Writing this letter to my son on his first birthday was one of the most therapeutic exercises I have ever done. I sat back and reflected on my birth story and the first time Matteo giggled. I thought about the first time we put him in his jolly jumper and the first time he said "Mama"! My, how fast a year goes! Every day I watch Matteo play, learn, and grow at lightning speed. I do not want to forget these incredible moments. I also look at Matteo now, well past one year old, and that letter seems even more special because I see how much he's grown since, and those particular recollections I chose to write about were merely a snapshot in time. Since then, an infinite amount of more milestones flood my memory. The infamous saying, "the days are long but the years are short," has never been so clear to me now. We work so hard each day exhausted by all our duties as mothers, but then we blink and our babies aren't so little anymore.

A CHALLENGE FOR YOU

Write a letter to your baby. Take the time to look back on your life with them. Think of how much growing they have done. Now think back on your life *before* them. What's even more amazing: how much growing *you* have done.

To get your writer's cap on, here are some ideas:

- Tell them about their birthing story.
- How did you feel when you brought your baby home from the hospital for the first time?
- How did you and your significant other adjust to parenthood?
- What are the daily quirks of your relationship with your baby that just melts your heart; those little things that make each day so special you wouldn't want to forget?
- Can you think of a funny/significant/heartfelt story you want to share?
- What about them learning a new skill or hitting a particular milestone?

- What are a few of your child's favourite things that showcase their personality?
- Who plays an important role in your baby's life? A family pet? A neighbour? A cousin?
- What brings them joy? How do they bring joy to other people?
- What advice would you give if your baby was to read this letter when they are expecting their first child?
- What do you hope for in your baby's future?

I opened this book with a letter to my readers and I will close this book with a letter to the love of my life, my everything, my reason for existence, my son, Matteo. I hope you found some laughter, some inspiration, and some support in the pages of this book. I write for all moms out there and I write as one perspective that I hope resonated with you and will help you to enjoy every moment of your time adjusting to motherhood. I write to educate, and I most certainly write to make sure you do not feel alone! Expect the challenges, but enjoy the journey. And don't forget to celebrate your successes every step of the way.

TO OUR BEAUTIFUL BOY MATTEO,

I cannot believe it, tomorrow is your first birthday!!! I sit here reminiscing on our first year together and I can honestly say it has been the most fulfilling, most joyous year of my life. Each day with you is so unbelievably special. You are cruising around like a toddler already, getting into cupboards, exploring the outdoors, climbing the stairs — you are a ball of energy, to say the least. I remember the day I delivered you. You were just a tiny little bundle at 7 pounds 4 ounces — the cutest little bundle your father and I had ever seen — how did you grow so fast?! You and I made a great team when it came to bringing you into the world. We worked hard to get you out of the comfort of my womb. Your dad was our biggest cheerleader and even though I was in labour for 23 hours, he was by my side every step of the way. I delivered you via c-section on April 21, 2019, at 3:43 am. Your Dad was so excited to finally have you in his arms, he couldn't stop smiling and taking pictures of you curled up on his chest. Seeing you for the first time was life-changing for the both of us.

Fast forward to current day and here you are one year old already; a happy, healthy, strong, handsome one year old. Since you were born, you have been an over-achiever; rolling over at two months, and taking your first steps by 10 months. You eat pretty much everything we give you, a big eater just like your mom and dad. My favourite part of every day is when we get to play together and I watch you learn new things. You have been walking for weeks now and that is about all you want to do! You play with your toys — throwing balls, playing with shapes, bulldozing block towers — but you get the most excited when you get to roam the house and play with our family dog, Leo. Leo loves you so much and lets you crawl all over him. Leo was a spoiled dog before you were born, but he adapted pretty quickly when we brought you home. He instantly became your big brother, always wanting to protect you. If you are

upstairs crying in your crib, Leo will lay outside your nursery waiting for someone to check on you. You two are definitely best friends.

Your most favourite toy right now is the television remote. We are not exactly sure why you love it so much, but sometimes you won't even leave the house without it. Each morning you will scurry into the living room to find it on the coffee table, and turn it over and over in your cute little chubby hands for hours. You smile every time you hear a little 'click!' when you press the buttons. You absolutely love books, so we read to you every day. Sometimes you make us read one book 10 times over before you move on to the next one. You are learning lots of words and will point to a picture and say "yellow" or "blue" or "green"- you are very smart! You love saying "Dadda" "Mama" "Grandpa" "Ya!" and are learning new words every single day. Sometimes you will grab our fingers and make us point to the picture. All these cute quirks make you the special Matteo that you are.

I write you this letter so that we can remember these special moments of our first year together. And to let you know that each smile, each giggle, each new milestone brings us so much joy. The way you have enriched our lives is indescribable, and you will only be able to understand this when you have children of your own. We wish for you a life of health and happiness. We wish for you many exciting adventures and countless fun memories.

We hope for you to every day feel loved by your parents, and to never feel alone, scared or sad.

Continue to grow and learn and fill your life with all the things that make you happy; cuddling your dog, reading your books, and maybe even just the sound of the "click!" of a button on the remote control.

We love you so much Matteo,

Love Mom and Dad

MORE MATERNAL MENTAL HEALTH INFO

Offered in chapter 1 is a basic understanding of pregnancy and postpartum depression and anxiety, but maternal mental health can be much more complicated than that. If you are looking for more information on other types of perinatal mood disorders including postpartum psychosis, postpartum anxiety disorders such as panic attacks and obsessive compulsive disorder and post-traumatic stress disorder, as well, options if you feel the need to seek out help I have included it in this section.

POSTPARTUM PSYCHOSIS

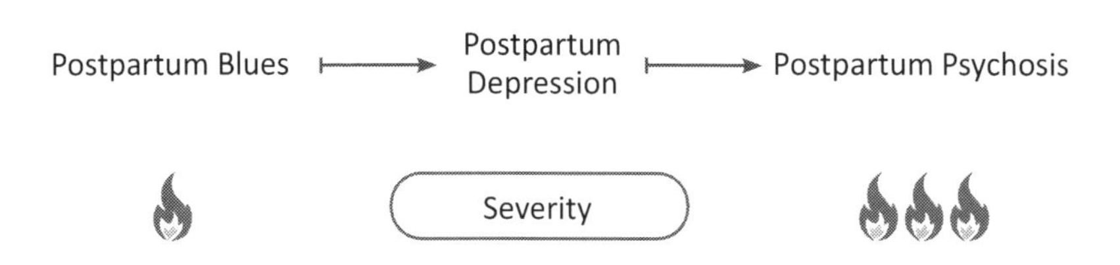

Feelings connected to PPD can be visualized on a scale. Think of it as a spectrum of severity, with baby blues on the far left, post-partum depression in the middle, and postpartum psychosis on the far right. Postpartum psychosis is considered the most extreme and detrimental diagnosis because mothers in this state can experience delusions, out of body experiences, and a loss of reality, though they are very rare. To complicate matters, this can occur very early on in the postpartum period — as early as 72 hours after delivery — and usually continues to be a substantial threat within the first two to four weeks after delivery, although, the risk is there at any time beyond the immediate postpartum period. Indisputably, **at any point that a mother is experiencing the following symptoms, consider it a medical emergency that requires immediate help:**

- Visual Hallucinations (seeing things that are not there)
- Auditory Hallucinations (hearing voices when nobody is around)
- Delusions (beliefs held with strong conviction despite conflicting evidence to the contrary. For example, a mother who attempts to harm her baby because she believes that her baby is the devil)
- Grandiosity Delusions (belief in having special abilities or powers)
- Control Delusions (belief of being controlled by forces or other individuals)
- Disordered Thoughts (illogical or chaotic thoughts)
- Disorganized Speech (moving quickly from one topic to the next or speaking with garbled, incomprehensible speech)
- Disordered Behaviours (disruptive or disorganized behaviours)[61]

ANXIETY DISORDER: PREGNANCY OR POSTPARTUM PANIC DISORDER

Some of us may experience a certain form of anxiety known as panic attacks. Though panic attacks are not as dangerous as they may feel at the time and will leave you unscathed, the feelings associated with these attacks are dreadful. Symptoms include:

- Chest pain
- Shortness of breath
- Dizziness
- Numbness and tingling of extremities[62]

ANXIETY DISORDER: PREGNANCY OR POSTPARTUM OBSESSIVE-COMPULSIVE DISORDER

It is thought that around two percent of women may experience symptoms of Postpartum Obsessive-Compulsive Disorder (POCD); this diagnosis also fits into the realm of a specific type of anxiety disorder. The obsessions in this diagnosis are recurrent unpleasant thoughts, impulses, or images and these thoughts may not make sense.

These obsessions are not considered the same as merely excessive worries about real-life problems; they are much more severe. It is common in POCD to have obsessions related explicitly to fears or images of harming your baby. People suffering from POCD may recognize that these obsessions are a product of their mind or imagination and try to ignore or suppress the obsessions. They may even attempt to neutralize obsessions with other thoughts or actions and will continue even though these thoughts are truly debilitating. It is the *compulsions* within this diagnosis, repetitive behaviours or mental acts, that are performed with the hope of diminishing the discomfort associated with the *obsessions*. Compulsions may take the form of rituals with rigid rules. For example, having to complete an action in a specific order or manner or repeating it a certain number of times would be considered a compulsion.

More examples of compulsions are:

- Obsessive cleaning (overly concerned about germs)
- Repeatedly checking on your baby (fear that something bad will happen)
- Minimizing interactions with your baby (fear of harming baby)

Women are at greater risk of experiencing POCD if they have a previous diagnosis of Obsessive-Compulsive Disorder (OCD) or a family history of it. Living with POCD severely interferes with the individual's routine and relationships, as compulsions can be extremely time-consuming and stress-inducing. Therefore, POCD that goes untreated can have negative effects on the bonding between mom and baby, as well as the mother's ability to cope.[63]

ANXIETY DISORDER: PREGNANCY OR POSTPARTUM POST-TRAUMATIC STRESS DISORDER

Similarly to post-traumatic stress disorder (PTSD) that is not linked to the postpartum period, this diagnosis is caused by a traumatic or fear-provoking experience. Specifically, pregnancy or postpartum post-traumatic stress disorder (PPTSD) is often related to a frightening childbirth experience or a past trauma. This diagnosis also falls within the anxiety family. Symptoms of

PPTSD may include:

- Flashbacks of the trauma in the form of intrusive memories or nightmares (particularly present in partnership with feelings of anxiety)
- Thoughts or behaviours that support avoidance of the reminder of the trauma
- Feelings of general numbing and detachment
- Sleep disturbances (brought on by your thoughts, not because you're woken up by your baby that needs to feed)
- Irritability
- Poor concentration
- Feeling 'on-edge' (easily startled)
- Highly sensitive to environmental stimuli
- Avoidant (especially for follow up medical care)
- Decreased ability (or avoidance) of bonding with your baby

Risk factors of PPTSD include, but are not limited to: a history of abuse (including childhood abuse that complicates feelings of becoming a parent), history of sexual abuse that may be triggered during pregnancy or labour and delivery, history of infertility, unanticipated outcomes of delivery (such as miscarriage or birth defects), and any type of traumatic or complicated birth experience in this pregnancy or previous pregnancies.[64]

It has been recognized that nearly one in five women carry symptoms of post-traumatic stress after giving birth, and acute PPTSD occurs in about 5-6% of the entire population. You could experience symptoms from your own experience, from witnessing a traumatic birth, or even hearing about a traumatic experience of someone else. It is also important to note that the feelings of what is considered traumatic are in the eyes of the beholder. In other words, if you believed it be traumatic, it could affect you no matter what others' opinions are of your experience.

As mentioned earlier, it is important to recognize that any type of anxiety disorder and depression can be experienced as simply one or the other, can be experienced simultaneously, or feelings of one can morph into feelings of the other. So now, going back to our diagram, let's add anxiety to the severity spectrum.

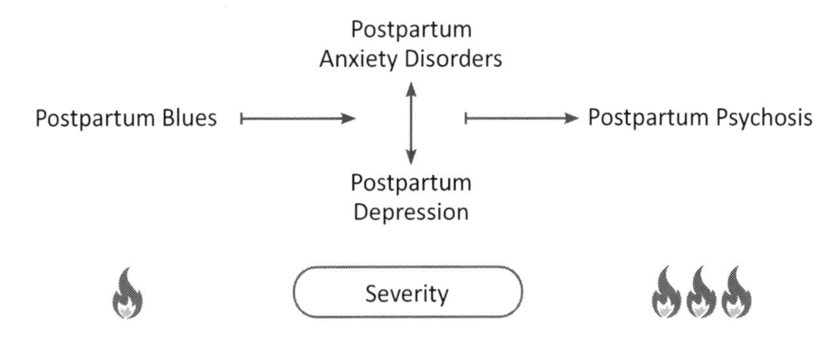

If you feel like you're experiencing any symptoms listed that are hindering your ability to function each day and cope, this is not a means to your end. It is most certainly possible to gain back control of your life with any of these diagnoses. It is also absolutely possible to recover from such disorders. First and foremost, if at any point you feel the need to reach out to someone surrounding your diagnosis — or potential diagnosis — there are so many resources out there for you!

WHERE TO GET HELP

- **Your Doctor**

  If at any point you feel the need to get assessed, please book an appointment with your doctor. Ask questions and be open to discuss your symptoms. This isn't the time to sugar coat, try and cover up your true feelings, or be a 'tough guy'— leave that for the mobsters in the movies. It's important for you, your baby, and your family to be completely transparent about what you are experiencing.

- **The Postpartum Support International**

  This is a non-profit organization dedicated to helping those suffering from perinatal mood and anxiety disorders by providing reliable information, is home to the best practice training, and has many volunteer coordinators within Canada, the United States, and 30 other countries around the world.

  Call or Text: 1-800-944-4PPD/ 1-800-944-4773 in North America

  Visit: www.postpartum.net to find resources within your area

- **National Crisis Text Line**

  To speak with a trained Crisis Responder anytime about any type of crisis

  Text: HOME to 686868 in Canada

  Text: HOME to 741741 in USA

- **National Suicide Prevention Hotline & Website**

  Call: 1-833-456-4566 in Canada

Call: 1-800-273-TALK / 1-800-273-8255 in USA

Visit: www.suicidepreventionlifeline.org

- **National Center for PTSD**

  To gain information about post-traumatic stress disorder or screen yourself for a possible diagnosis.

  Visit: www.ptsd.va.gov

  Visit: https://www.emdr.com for more information regarding EMDR as a treatment option for trauma

- **Public Health Agencies**

  Though I cannot speak to every city, town, state, province, or country, I recommend that you look into the community services available in your area. Within my community, there are a lot of services available (such as a hotline for health-related questions specific to the postpartum period) and a ton of information on our Provincial Public Health website.

- **Online Resources and Support Groups**

  There are so many online communities full of new mothers supporting one another. Look for Facebook groups, Instagram accounts dedicated to perinatal mental health, or mom blogs. Search for particulars for your situation to get the most out of your supports such as "postpartum depression and raising twins." You may be surprised at how many other mamas are going through whatever it is that you are feeling.

APPENDIX A

Edinburgh Perinatal/Postnatal Depression Scale (EPDS)

For use between **28–32 weeks** in **all** pregnancies and **6–8 weeks** postpartum

Name: ______________________ Date: ____________ Gestation in Weeks: _____

As you are having a baby, we would like to know how you are feeling. Please mark "X" in the box next to the answer which comes closest to how you have felt in the **past 7 days**—not just how you feel today.

In the past 7 days:

1. I have been able to laugh and see the funny side of things
   - 0 As much as I always could
   - 1 Not quite so much now
   - 2 Definitely not so much now
   - 3 Not at all
2. I have looked forward with enjoyment to things
   - 0 As much as I ever did
   - 1 Rather less than I used to
   - 2 Definitely less than I used to
   - 3 Hardly at all
3. I have blamed myself unnecessarily when things went wrong
   - 3 Yes, most of the time
   - 2 Yes, some of the time
   - 1 Not very often
   - 0 No, never
4. I have been anxious or worried for no good reason
   - 0 No, not at all
   - 1 Hardly ever
   - 2 Yes, sometimes
   - 3 Yes, very often
5. I have felt scared or panicky for no very good reason
   - 3 Yes, quite a lot
   - 2 Yes, sometimes
   - 1 No, not much
   - 0 No, not at all
6. Things have been getting on top of me
   - 3 Yes, most of the time I haven't been able to cope
   - 2 Yes, sometimes I haven't been coping as well as usual
   - 1 No, most of the time I have coped quite well
   - 0 No, I have been coping as well as ever
7. I have been so unhappy that I have had difficulty sleeping
   - 3 Yes, most of the time
   - 2 Yes, sometimes
   - 1 Not very often
   - 0 No, not at all
8. I have felt sad or miserable
   - 3 Yes, most of the time
   - 2 Yes, quite often
   - 1 Not very often
   - 0 No, not at all
9. I have been so unhappy that I have been crying
   - 3 Yes, most of the time
   - 2 Yes, quite often
   - 1 Only occasionally
   - 0 No, never
10. The thought of harming myself has occurred to me
    - 3 Yes, quite often
    - 2 Sometimes
    - 1 Hardly ever
    - 0 Never

Total Score

Edinburgh Perinatal/Postnatal Depression Scale (EPDS)

SCORING GUIDE

1. I have been able to laugh and see the funny side of things
   - **0** As much as I always could
   - **1** Not quite so much now
   - **2** Definitely not so much now
   - **3** Not at all
2. I have looked forward with enjoyment to things
   - **0** As much as I ever did
   - **1** Rather less than I used to
   - **2** Definitely less than I used to
   - **3** Hardly at all
3. I have blamed myself unnecessarily when things went wrong
   - **3** Yes, most of the time
   - **2** Yes, some of the time
   - **1** Not very often
   - **0** No, never
4. I have been anxious or worried for no good reason
   - **0** No, not at all
   - **1** Hardly ever
   - **2** Yes, sometimes
   - **3** Yes, very often
5. I have felt scared or panicky for no very good reason
   - **3** Yes, quite a lot
   - **2** Yes, sometimes
   - **1** No, not much
   - **0** No, not at all
6. Things have been getting on top of me
   - **3** Yes, most of the time I haven't been able to cope
   - **2** Yes, sometimes I haven't been coping as well as usual
   - **1** No, most of the time I have coped quite well
   - **0** No, I have been coping as well as ever
7. I have been so unhappy that I have had difficulty sleeping
   - **3** Yes, most of the time
   - **2** Yes, sometimes
   - **1** Not very often
   - **0** No, not at all
8. I have felt sad or miserable
   - **3** Yes, most of the time
   - **2** Yes, quite often
   - **1** Not very often
   - **0** No, not at all
9. I have been so unhappy that I have been crying
   - **3** Yes, most of the time
   - **2** Yes, quite often
   - **1** Only occasionally
   - **0** No, never
10. The thought of harming myself has occurred to me
    - **3** Yes, quite often
    - **2** Sometimes
    - **1** Hardly ever
    - **0** Never

EPDS Score	Interpretation	Action
Less than 8	Depression not likely	Continue support
9–11	Depression possible	Support, re-screen in 2–4 weeks. Consider referral to primary care provider (PCP).
12–13	Fairly high possibility of depression	Monitor, support and offer education. Refer to PCP.
14 and higher (positive screen)	Probable depression	Diagnostic assessment and treatment by PCP and/or specialist.
Positive score (1, 2 or 3) on question 10 (suicidality risk)		Immediate discussion required. Refer to PCP ± mental health specialist or emergency resource for further assessment and intervention as appropriate. Urgency of referral will depend on several factors including: whether the suicidal ideation is accompanied by a plan, whether there has been a history of suicide attempts, whether symptoms of a psychotic disorder are present and/or there is concern about harm to the baby.

Cox, J. L., J. M. Holden, and R. Sagovsky. "Edinburgh Postnatal Depression Scale." *PsycTESTS Dataset*, 1987. https://doi.org/10.1037/t01756-000.

THE QUICK 'N DIRTY OF GRAB THE BROOM

CHAPTER 1

Making Sense of Maternal Mental Health

Is What We're Feeling Normal?

- Virtually all women have the potential to develop a mood disorder during pregnancy or within the first year after delivery. No woman is entirely and wholly protected from the physiological, emotional, and psychological changes that accompany life after having a baby.
- We are taught that motherhood and bad feelings do not mix. Ever. So, when sadness starts creeping up on us and we cry for no apparent reason, we may feel a little caught off-guard.
- The truth is, although we may imagine mothering to be an instinctual ability that we hold deep inside of us, it is still a journey of lifelong learning. There are days we question our capabilities, days we lose confidence in ourselves, days we struggle to perform effortlessly, and days we feel unfavourable emotions even when they are logically unwarranted. This is natural.

Baby blues

- Is a normal hormonal adjustment in the immediate postpartum period.
- Can last up to two weeks.
- Is not considered a medical condition and does not require a medical intervention. It does, however, require support and understanding from those around you.
- Simply put, if getting through the day is seemingly an impossible task for you after two weeks postpartum and you are absolutely debilitated by undesirable feelings, it is time to seek help.

Common pregnancy or postpartum depression (PPD) symptoms:

- A lack of interest in your baby
- Immense irritability or anger
- Crying and sadness that have surpassed the first two weeks after your delivery, including feelings of hopelessness, strong guilt, or shame
- Changes in appetite (overeating or a loss of appetite)
- Sleep disturbances (brought on by your thoughts, not because you're woken up by your baby that needs to feed)
- Loss of pleasure or interest in things that you used to enjoy doing or being a part of
- Thoughts of causing harm to yourself or your baby

Common pregnancy or postpartum anxiety (PPA) symptoms:

- Severe and constant worries and fears (often related to the health and safety of your baby)
- A persistent uneasiness that something bad is going to happen
- Racing thoughts
- Thoughts about death (fearing death due to perceived danger)
- Changes in appetite (overeating or a loss of appetite)
- Sleep disturbances (brought on by thoughts, not because you are being woken by your baby that needs to feed)
- Inability to sit still
- Dizziness
- Hot flashes
- Nausea

For where to get help turn to page 195

CHAPTER 2

You are New and Improved... Embrace It!

Life, as you Know it, is Forever Changed

- Having a baby changes your life.
- With change, if you are moving in the right direction, then the benefit of what's to come will be more significant than whatever it is you're giving up.
- Understand that your life is different with a baby and take

the time to see what that means to you.

- Recognize and embrace your evolution into motherhood as you alter your mindset, your outlook, and your priorities.
- Allow your significant other to adjust to parenthood in their own right too; this doesn't always happen simultaneously between two parents.

CHAPTER 3

Who's in Your Mama Crew?

Finding a Support System

- Build a support system with other mothers. Ask lots of questions. Don't isolate yourself!
- Research has found that community supports are the most influential factor and most beneficial aspect of treatment for women who are experiencing postpartum depression and postpartum anxiety.
- As a new mother, it's important to surround yourself with people that provide you with the support that you need. When adding to your support system ask yourself:

1. Does _________ bring positivity into my life?
2. Does _________ respect my values?
3. How does ________ support me in my journey?

THE CHALLENGE IN THIS CHAPTER

Over the next month, with each encounter you have with someone, write down the qualities they possess that bring significance into your world. Then, ask them to do the same about you and what qualities you bring to the table. Remember, friendship is a two-way street. Do *your* share to make a companionship an enriching exchange, and in turn, you can create substantial and valuable connections. Know the value true friendship can bring to your life.

CHAPTER 4

Can You See the Rainbow?

Seeking out Gratitude

- We will all feel pain and unbearable sadness one day as we navigate through life, but we can also trust that we will be able to find a blessing or two within our journeys.
- We all have stories that change who we are — at the core of our being — but that doesn't give us a free pass on the sympathy train. I dare you to look for the positive in the sea of dark, the rainbow within the storm.
- Blessings are considered something beneficial for which one is grateful. That means a blessing can be *anything at all*.

THE CHALLENGE IN THIS CHAPTER

At the end of each day write down three blessings that you have in your life. Maybe it is something that you experienced on that particular day that resonated with you. Maybe it is just something, or someone, in your life that you are grateful for. Do this exercise for 30 days, with the goal that this will become a habit in your life and change your way of thinking. The most important step to creating a habit is *consistency*. So, once you have done this exercise for 30 days, do it for another 30 days and then another.

The second part to this challenge: recite those three blessings that you wrote down the night before. Start your day off by reminding yourself of what you were grateful for yesterday. Opening your day to feelings of gratitude sets your intention for the rest of the day and that's one small – but momentous – practice for a healthy mindset.

CHAPTER 5

The Power of a Little Fresh Air

Getting the Heck Out of your House

- Get out and smell the roses. I mean this figuratively — let's appreciate what is often ignored as the analogy suggests — but I also mean this literally. Get out of your house and spend time outdoors. I promise you will feel better. Seriously, it is that simple.
- The more you practice getting out of the house, the easier it will become.
- Staying inside and away from others is considered a coping mechanism of our minds, though we may not even be cognizant of this.
- When we are feeling anxious or depressed, our minds tell our bodies that we are safest within our "box" and anything outside of these abstract boundaries of safety is full of the unknown.

- The familiarity of our box can be comforting but the problem with avoidance is it never gives you the chance to challenge your thoughts.
- We have to interrupt those thoughts of fearfulness that may cause untruths to become our reality. If you never defy your feelings, then that's the existence you have created and the truth that you live in.

THE CHALLENGE IN THIS CHAPTER

When learning how to get out of the house with a baby on time start with setting a goal for yourself. For example, *"I want to get out of the house by 11 am today."* Practice with a plan that doesn't have a specific start time. Do this when your calendar is wide open and you have no responsibilities to anyone other than yourself and the schedule of your newborn because, well, that is hard enough. Keep track of how much time it takes for you to pack the diaper bag, change your baby's diaper, put your own pants on (don't forget your pants!), probably change another diaper, and get out of the house. Continue to practice it again and again until you recognize, roughly, the amount of time it takes for you to get out of the house with a baby. Now, add an extra 15 minutes to your estimated time and use *that* as your baseline for any future plans.

CHAPTER 6

"Moms Are Selfish," Said No One Ever

Selflessness Begins with Selfishness

- Taking care of yourself is imperative. Without healthy moms, how are we going to raise healthy babies in healthy households?
- You cannot be the best mother to your children when you completely cut yourself off of any self-love.
- Babies feel our emotions. Not only are our babies cognizant of our stress, but they also have physiological changes of their own in reaction to our stress, described as *emotional contagion*.
- You are the best mom to your baby when you are the best version of yourself.

Healthy Self-Care Suggestions

- Yoga
- Meditation
- Exercise
- Journaling
- Reading
- Social groups or sports teams
- Quality time with pets

THE FIRST CHALLENGE IN THIS CHAPTER

Brainstorm ideas on how you can make time in your schedule for a little self-care. Is there someone you can utilize to babysit so that it's possible to take action on some "me-time"?

THE SECOND CHALLENGE IN THIS CHAPTER

During your next interaction, be cognizant of the emotions that the other person is portraying. Reflect on how you reacted to their emotion during the encounter and then take the time to reflect on how you feel after.

CHAPTER 7

Being Present

Preparing for Life while Demolishing Expectations

- We can prepare, but we need to be adaptable. It is our *expectations* of the future that give us feelings of anxiety. We want to be in control.
- The practice of non-attachment is the state in which we overcome our connection to relationships, material objects, and ideas we live by to attain a sharpened and more beneficial outlook of the world.
- The ideas behind non-attachment support us to diminish our union to the relationships of all things in our lives. It does not require us to give up our goals or desires and it doesn't

mean we are not challenged by certain news or situations. It compels us to be cognizant of when we relate our happiness to the attachment of an idea we want to live up to.

- To understand non-attachment, we need to recognize the fluidity of all things in our world. Absolutely nothing in life is stagnant, nothing is permanent, and simply anticipating that change will occur in all aspects of life will allow us to accept our evolution more easily. Learning to flow with the variability of life enables us to enjoy the experience for what is it without an expectation that it will always be.
- In the world of motherhood, non-attachment teaches us to release any expected outcomes of our parenting journey.

THE CHALLENGE IN THIS CHAPTER

Think about a significant part of your journey (it could be anything at all: your fertility journey, your pregnancy, labour or delivery, or any aspect of motherhood you have experienced thus far) that you did not anticipate happening as it did. Expectations are everywhere and along every step of our experiences. Once you pinpoint a significant event, write down all the expectations you had surrounding it. Read it over. The next step: throw that piece of paper in the trash.

Now for part two, let's practice gratitude. Once again, identify what you are grateful for within that same situation you identified in the first part of this exercise. What can you identify as a blessing, even though the experience did not play out as you had hoped?

CHAPTER 8

PAUSE

Doing your (Proper) Research

- We are privileged to be experiencing motherhood during a time in which we can be educated on anything we need to know and as quickly as we need to know it.
- Not only can we gain health-related information, get reassurance about the health of our babies, or be better prepared before seeking a medical opinion, there are also numerous support groups, blogs, and websites dedicated specifically to our community of mothers.
- Unfortunately, the time in history that social media and other technological platforms began to rule our way of life correlates directly to the skyrocketing rates of anxiety, depression, and suicide we are witnessing within our society.
- Let's educate ourselves on how to educate ourselves.
- While I am searching and when I am looking for information online, I always take the time to **P.A.U.S.E.**

I ask myself: What is the ***P****urpose of this site? What are the* ***A****uthor's credentials? Is the information* ***U****p-to-date? Is the wording* ***S****imple enough for me to understand? When I* ***E****xplore other credible sites, do I find similar information?*

- **P**urpose of the Site
- **A**uthor's Credentials
- **U**p-to-date information
- **S**implicity
- **E**xplore other sites to cross-check information

CHAPTER 9:

It's All Up to Mama

Being Empowered by the Power of Choice

- The power of choice is empowering. The power of choice is also taxing. It is a topic that brings angst to many new moms. Being responsible for another human life, well that's a big undertaking and it comes with *a lot* of decisions to be made.
- It is proven that satisfaction in life declines when options increase because we become heightened to the opportunities we've given up or that we may be missing out on. The more options we have in front of us creates anxiety in the fact that when we pick a path we don't know if we have chosen the right one or if we could be happier doing something different.
- Let's break down the process of decision-making into some easy-to-follow steps. This approach is known as our motherhood decision tree (MDT).
- **Step 1:** Know your end goal
- **Step 2:** Identify your values
- **Step 3:** Do your research
- **Step 4:** Weight your options
- **Step 5:** Make your verdict
- And always be flexible!

CHAPTER 10

Are We All Just a Bunch of Imposters?

Oh, the Mom Guilt!

- Mom guilt is characterized by this overpowering, gut-wrenching feeling of regret over something we did or didn't do that *we think* has failed our children.
- Mom guilt is a product of the doubt we feel in our capabilities. We feel this uncertainty because we second-guess our parenting abilities.
- Imposter Mom Syndrome is the thought that we don't feel that we know enough about mothering to be a mother, so we don't trust ourselves. Even when there is no reason not to. There is this belief out there that we are wired to be textbook parents and that our capabilities are born alongside our child. I have to tell you a secret: all new moms feel this way and there isn't a single mom out there that knows everything about parenthood.

THE CHALLENGE IN THIS CHAPTER

Anytime you are quick to judge a "screw up" you did as a mom, take a moment to identify two things you did successfully that same day. To take this one step further, anytime you are quick to judge *another* mom's "screw up", acknowledge two things she did great. Tell her these achievements you witnessed and spread that kindness and support.

CHAPTER 11

Becoming Your Own Body Guard

Managing your Influences

- Throughout our daily lives, we are constantly being bombarded with influences that bring up emotions in us that may be constructive or — on the flip side — damaging to our well-being. Being in a vulnerable state, such as the transition into motherhood, what you expose yourself to can take an even greater toll on your mental health.
- Think about what you watch, listen to, follow, who you speak to, whatever it may be that adversely influences your feelings after your interaction.
- It is proven that the release of oxytocin actually increases our ability to read faces and emotions. Instinctually, this heightened state we enter aids us in our ability to interact with our babies and to respond to their needs, but it plays a role in *all* the interactions we are exposed to.
- Though we cannot avoid certain individuals, we can limit our exposure when we feel it is detrimental to our well-being. For instance, abiding by a strict timeline for a particular visit may be important for you. Set a maximum amount of time you spend with your company and then when the time is up, no matter what the circumstances, say your good-byes and depart. Advise them beforehand that you will need to leave by a certain time so that there are no surprises when you start heading toward the exit. Too much time with particular people can sometimes weaken boundaries and cause rifts in relationships or lead to unpleasant interactions. Know your limits. In other circumstances,

acknowledge when you aren't feeling rested or resilient and avoid interactions altogether.

- Emotional agility is an individual's ability to experience their thoughts and emotions and events in a way that doesn't drive them in negative ways, but instead encourages them to reveal the best of themselves.

To work toward emotional agility:

- *Face your real feelings*
- *Detach from your emotions*
- *Match your feelings to your core values*
- *Set your goals*

THE CHALLENGE IN THIS CHAPTER

In a 24-hour period, keep track and list out everything you spent time focusing on: television shows, the people you conversed with, your social media feed and online influences, etc. Beside each, write down how you felt after the interaction. Is what you're focusing on and putting your energy toward helping or hindering your well-being? Do you have an abundance of constructive influences, or are most of them unhealthy? Now I ask you: how can you change your daily habits to decrease feelings that feed into your angst?

CHAPTER 12

My Priority Cherry Pie

Prioritizing your Endless Responsibilities

- It takes a village to raise a baby! Don't try to do it all yourself.
- Follow these guidelines for your priority pie of chaos:

    1. Each day represents a fresh priority pie, and it is always prepped the night before.
    2. Each pie will look different than the last.
    3. Once you are "full", you must put your pie away, no matter how much of it is left. Some days you may devour it all, while other days you may struggle to finish half or even less. It doesn't matter how much you finish; what matters is — as the saying goes — to never bite off more than you can chew.
    4. Never divide your pie up into more than six slices.
    5. At least one slice each day is meant to uplift you.
    6. Be sure to eat a variety of slices to nurture yourself holistically.

- *Question:* How do I get through my to-do list when there aren't enough hours in a day?

  Answer: We don't need to do it all in a day.

- *Question:* If I have come to realize I can't do it all, how can I figure a way to live a life that supports what is important to me?

  Answer: Do this Challenge:

THE FIRST CHALLENGE IN THIS CHAPTER

Spend a few days tracking where you spend your time. This will give you an idea of how much of your day you are devoting to the responsibilities in your life including family, friends, health, home, work, yourself, etc. Recognizes that the areas where you spend the most time should match what you value the most.

The next part is to then identify and link each task to a particular type of energy: physical, emotional, spiritual, and mental to learn how you are draining your energy.

- *Question:* How much should I expect from myself as a new mom and when am I pushing myself to a point that is unhealthy for my well-being?

  Answer: We have that right to not do everything we are humanly capable of all the time. So let this advice permit you to sometimes take a breather without feeling any guilt.

  "Hara Hachi bu" which means stop eating when you are 80% full. Although this advice is dedicated to living longer through healthier eating practices, being the foodie that I am, I say that this applies to our mental health just the same! When you have had enough for one day, put your tasks list away.

- *Question:* Is there ever going to be a way to fit some time in a day for **me**?

  Answer: The priorities we identify each day should not only be chores or those dreadful tasks we just have to get done. Prioritize you. Prioritize your rest, physical activity, or any other self-care options that help you recharge, and write it down as one of your pie slices.

ANOTHER CHALLENGE IN THIS CHAPTER

Since there is always more to do in our busy lives, I challenge you to find a way to pass off one of your responsibilities. As often as possible, share a piece of your priority pie with someone else. To do so, you may need to get a little creative. Try though to avoid passing off to anyone who also has a newborn; which means don't go directly to your significant other all the time. Look for outside sources and it also shouldn't always have to cost money.

CHAPTER 13

Let's Get Physical!

Giving your Body what She Needs

- I would like to give some of the spotlight to our physical body. Specifically, let's focus on our mind-body connection and speak to the influence that our physical health can have on our mental well-being.
- Take as long as you need to heal, rest and recover after giving birth.
- Knowing what I know now, I can say with honesty that a major regret of mine after the birth of my baby was not slowing down in life to really take the time to prioritize recovery and bonding with Matteo. *For as long I needed.* That should be what matters in the postpartum period.

Strategies:

1. Resting
2. Cuddles and bonding time
3. Nourishment/healthy eating
4. Movement/exercise

CHAPTER 14

CHILL OUT

How to Pull Yourself out of Unproductive Anxiety

- Our breath is a symptom of every emotion, a constant throughout our entire life and with us wherever we are. If we can learn to navigate and manage our breath we can navigate any situation in life.
- Follow this three step strategy when anxiety is getting the best of you:

Step 1: Interference

- *Change of Scenery*
- *Change of Temperature*
- *Five, Four, Three, Two, One*
- *Utilize your Support System*
- *Distraction Activities*

Step 2: Challenge

- It's important to ask yourself if the thoughts that are in your mind are facts.

Step 3: Recovery

- Step one is to change your immediate thoughts, step three is to foster your resiliency and build up your armour.

- So how with these three steps are we CHILLin' OUT?

  C: commit to

  H: healing by causing

  I: interference on those anxious thoughts. Use

  L: logic and

  L: love for yourself to

  O: oppose anxious ideas and then

  U: unwind with

  T: therapeutic exercises.

THE CHALLENGE IN THIS CHAPTER

Set an alarm for a couple of random times throughout the day. When your alarm goes off, no matter where you are, take a few moments to stop and reflect on what you are doing and how you are feeling. Now focus on your breath. Take the time to see if your feelings and your actions are related to stress or if you are calm and relaxed. If you are noticing some tension, close your eyes and take five deep, refreshing, and resetting breaths before you continue on your day. With each breath count to four as you fill your lungs all the way to full capacity and then four again as you completely exhale your breath all the way out. The point of this exercise is to ground us back to a calm state by simply being cognizant of our feelings and using our breath to reset ourselves.

CHAPTER 15

When Things Aren't as You had Hoped

Dealing with Unexpected Challenges

- It should come as no surprise that postpartum depression and anxiety can be triggered when you are faced with unanticipated hardships with your child because this can lead to providing extra care, fearing what the future holds, making life-altering decisions, dealing with emotional strain, and so much more.
- Many new parents are terrified of the challenges they may be faced with, but when I say that every child is a blessing and what we can learn from every one of them is immense, I mean this wholeheartedly.
- If you are someone who is going through a particular struggle – whatever that may be – and having a difficult time navigating life, the first step I ask of you is to learn as much as you can and to find a community that will support you in your journey.
- Remember: the biggest challenges can lead to the most special outcomes.

Some other actions that may help you if you are going through a particular challenge:

- *Express your emotions to the healthcare staff/your support system and they will educate you.*
- *Ask lots of questions.*
- *Keep a journal of the journey.*
- *While being respectful of others' opinions, such as family members, practice saying no unapologetically, even if they*

push their opinions and judgments onto you after you have made your decision.

- *Take some space from those who are not supporting you in a way you feel you need to be supported.*
- *Trust yourself to make decisions for your family.*
- *Make time for self-care.*
- We are not in control of what difficulties we will be faced with, but we are responsible for how we live through it. We are responsible for how we choose to interpret these events in our lives.
- As much as we think seeking out a problem-free life is what we need to strive for, the most struggling times can be the most meaningful experiences. There is no such thing as a life without challenges!
- Seek out the blessings, find the meaning, and look for the growth and the strength that enters your life. We can improve our overall happiness to have challenges in life that we endure.
- Feeling victim means we feel hopeless, out of control, and cheated in some way that we did not deserve. Survivors feel resiliency, a sense of achievement, and triumph. What outlook do you want to have?

THE CHALLENGE IN THIS CHAPTER

If you are struggling with trauma from your birthing journey, write it out. Write it out as soon as you recognize you are haunted from one part or another and while it's fresh in your mind. Write what happened, how you felt, and what surprised you. Tuck it away somewhere and come back to it in six weeks. How do you feel about your journey now? Is it still something that haunts you? Do you still carry strong feelings of regret or feelings of being out of control? Do you still feel the need to heal from your experience? Re-write your experience to see if you now carry a different recollection of events, in a more positive light. Maybe you look at your beautiful baby who is growing and learning and you have come to realize that everything happened just as it should.

Though I would love to write a book to each person individually as to what they need to overcome their struggles or the trauma they suffered, our journeys are too unique for this to be possible. That said, I promise there are options for you if you feel the need to heal mentally, physically, or emotionally from your birthing experience. There are counsellors out there, healers, doctors, and therapists. You may have friends who could listen to your story and cry with you if that's what you feel you need. Having the ability to just talk it out sometimes can be beneficial for your healing. There are also strategies such as meditation, mindfulness, journaling, exposure therapy, and other therapy, such as cognitive behavioural therapy and EMDR, which are very effective to overcome trauma. Sometimes merely time is all that is needed to heal your wounds.

A LETTER TO MATTEO:

- As new moms, we have so many emotions and writing can be a way to sort through them. It can help to delve into what you are feeling and find sense within them.

THE CHALLENGE IN THIS CHAPTER

Write a letter to your baby. Take the time to look back on your life with them. Think of how much growing they have done. Now think back on your life before them. What's even more amazing is how much growing *you* have done.

ACKNOWLEDGEMENTS

First and foremost I must acknowledge my son, Matteo, for being the obvious inspiration and the star of this book. He has taught me more than I could ever imagine and, though I am candid about my struggles, becoming a mom has been the most extraordinary experience of my life.

Of course, my husband, Ryan, deserves a big shout out. He entered into parenthood alongside me and he really does make this journey that much more fun and exciting. I couldn't imagine anyone else by my side. I want to thank him for allowing me to share his struggles. It takes a special man to be so open and honest about the challenges we have been faced with.

All my girlfriends that have given me advice, stories to share, content for this book, and strategies to help other moms, I thank all of you! My first year of motherhood has been so special, having you all by my side. I do believe that my love for all of you and the strength you have given me is apparent in these chapters.

My parents, Chris and Lorayne and my siblings Kelly, Stephen, and Daniel. My family supports are so strong I don't know how I would get through this crazy world without my unique bond with each and every one of you.

My in-laws, Max and Paola, thank you for loving Matteo as much as I do and always be willing to help out my family at any given moment. You have given us incredible support as Ryan and I transition into parenthood.

Lastly, my editor, Rebecca, who helped me get my work into a finished product. It was so much more fun to have someone on this writing journey with me and I thank you for all your expertise. The end result wouldn't have been the same without you.

BIBLIOGRAPHY

1. "Maternal Mental Health." World Health Organization. World Health Organization. Accessed May 22, 2020. https://www.who.int/teams/mental-health-and-substance-use/maternal-mental-health.

2. Nicolson, Paula. "Loss, Happiness and Postpartum Depression: The Ultimate Paradox." *Canadian Psychology/Psychologie canadienne* 40, no. 2 (1999): 162–78. https://doi.org/10.1037/h0086834.

3. "Learn More: Postpartum Support International (PSI)." Postpartum Support International - PSI. Accessed May 22, 2020. https://www.postpartum.net/learn-more/.

4. Gruen, Dawn S. "Postpartum Depression: A Debilitating Yet Often Unassessed Problem." *Health & Social Work* 15, no. 4 (1990): 261–70. https://doi.org/10.1093/hsw/15.4.261.

5. Alexander, Elizabeth M., and Linda McMullen. "Constructions of Motherhood and Fatherhood in Newspaper Articles on Maternal and Paternal Postpartum Depression." *Gender and Language* 9, no. 2 (2014): 143–66. https://doi.org/10.1558/genl.v9i2.17318.

6. Gruen, Dawn S. “Postpartum Depression: A Debilitating Yet Often Unassessed Problem.” *Health & Social Work* 15, no. 4 (1990): 261–70. https://doi.org/10.1093/hsw/15.4.261.

7. Pawluski, Jodi L., Joseph S. Lonstein, and Alison S. Fleming. “The Neurobiology of Postpartum Anxiety and Depression.” *Trends in Neurosciences* 40, no. 2 (2017): 106–20. https://doi.org/10.1016/j.tins.2016.11.009.

8. Gruen, Dawn S. “Postpartum Depression: A Debilitating Yet Often Unassessed Problem.” *Health & Social Work* 15, no. 4 (1990): 261–70. https://doi.org/10.1093/hsw/15.4.261.

9. Mollard, Elizabeth. “Exploring Paradigms in Postpartum Depression Research: The Need for Feminist Pragmatism.” *Health Care for Women International* 36, no. 4 (2014): 378–91. https://doi.org/10.1080/07399332.2014.903951.

10. Wardrop, Andrea, and Natalee Popadiuk. “Women’s Experiences with Postpartum Anxiety: Expectations, Relationships, and Sociocultural Influences.” *The Qualitative Report*, 2015. https://doi.org/10.46743/2160-3715/2013.1564.

11. “Postpartum and Antepartum Anxiety: Postpartum Support - PSI: Postpartum Support International (PSI).” Postpartum Support International - PSI. Accessed May 22, 2020. https://www.postpartum.net/learn-more/anxiety/.

12. “Reproductive Mental Health.” Risks | Reproductive Mental Health: Supporting BC women’s mental health before, during and after pregnancy. Accessed August 4, 2020. https://reproductivementalhealth.ca/anxiety/risks.

13. Shetty, Jay. *Think like a Monk: Train Your Mind for Peace and Purpose Every Day*. New York: Simon & Schuster, 2020.

14. Shetty, Jay. *Think like a Monk: Train Your Mind for Peace and Purpose Every Day*. New York: Simon & Schuster, 2020.

15. Phillips, Sally, and Lesley Pitt. "Maternal Mental Health: Making a Difference." *Aotearoa New Zealand Social Work* 23, no. 3 (2016): 31–37. https://doi.org/10.11157/anzswj-vol23iss3id158.

16. Hollis, Rachel. *Girl, Stop Apologizing*. HarperCollins Leadership, 2019.

17. Kendall-Tackett, Kathleen. "Birth Trauma: The Causes and Consequences of Childbirth-Related PTSD." Praeclarus Press, June 4, 2021.

18. Waters, Sara F., Tessa V. West, and Wendy Berry Mendes. "Stress Contagion: Physiological Covariation between Mothers and Infants." *Psychological Science* 25, no. 4 (2014): 934.

19. Greenley, Rachel. "How do I detach myself from superficial objects and circumstances?," *Dear Maddi* (blog), March 5, 2020, https://www.ualberta.ca/science/student-services/student-life-engagement/wellness-matters/dear-maddi/2020/march/detach-superficial-objects.htmls.

20. Luna, Aletheia. "6 Ways to Practice Non-Attachment (and Find Inner Peace)," *Lonerwolf* (blog), March 4, 2021, https://lonerwolf.com/non-attachment/.

21. Luna, Aletheia. "6 Ways to Practice Non-Attachment (and Find Inner Peace)," *Lonerwolf* (blog), March 4, 2021, https://lonerwolf.com/non-attachment/.

22. Greenley, Rachel. "How do I detach myself from superficial objects and circumstances?," *Dear Maddi* (blog), March 5, 2020, https://www.ualberta.ca/science/student-services/student-life-engagement/wellness-matters/dear-maddi/2020/march/detach-superficial-objects.htmls.

23. Alexander, Elizabeth M., and Linda McMullen. "Constructions of Motherhood and Fatherhood in Newspaper Articles on Maternal and Paternal Postpartum Depression." *Gender and Language* 9, no. 2 (2014): 143–66. https://doi.org/10.1558/genl.v9i2.17318

24. Shetty, Jay. *Think like a Monk: Train Your Mind for Peace and Purpose Every Day*. New York: Simon & Schuster, 2020.

25. Afful-Dadzie, Eric, Stephen Nabareseh, Zuzana Komínková Oplatková, and Petr Klímek. "Model for Assessing Quality of Online Health Information: A Fuzzy VIKOR Based Method." *Journal of Multi-Criteria Decision Analysis* 23, no. 1-2 (2015): 49–62. https://doi.org/10.1002/mcda.1558.

26. Afful-Dadzie, Eric, Stephen Nabareseh, Zuzana Komínková Oplatková, and Petr Klímek. "Model for Assessing Quality of Online Health Information: A Fuzzy VIKOR Based Method." *Journal of Multi-Criteria Decision Analysis* 23, no. 1-2 (2015): 49–62. https://doi.org/10.1002/mcda.1558.

27. Afful-Dadzie, Eric, Stephen Nabareseh, Zuzana Komínková Oplatková, and Petr Klímek. "Model for Assessing Quality of Online Health Information: A Fuzzy VIKOR Based Method." *Journal of Multi-Criteria Decision Analysis* 23, no. 1-2 (2015): 49–62. https://doi.org/10.1002/mcda.1558.

28. Lindgaard, Gitte, Gary Fernandes, Cathy Dudek, and J. Brown. "Attention Web Designers: You Have 50 Milliseconds to Make a Good First Impression!" *Behaviour & Information Technology* 25, no. 2 (2006): 115–26. https://doi.org/10.1080/01449290500330448.

29. Charbonneau, Deborah H. "Health Disclaimers and Website Credibility Markers: Guidance for Consumer Health Reference in the Affordable Care Act Era." *Reference & User Services Quarterly* 54, no. 3 (2015): 30–36. https://doi.org/10.5860/rusq.54n3.30.

30. Nădăşan, Valentin. "The Quality of Online Health-Related Information – an Emergent Consumer Health Issue." *Acta Medica Marisiensis* 62, no. 4 (2016): 408–21. https://doi.org/10.1515/amma-2016-0048.

31. Roberts, Lorraine. "Health Information and the Internet: The 5 Cs Website Evaluation Tool." *British Journal of Nursing* 19, no. 5 (2010): 322–25. https://doi.org/10.12968/bjon.2010.19.5.47075.

32. Nădăşan, Valentin. "The Quality of Online Health-Related Information – an Emergent Consumer Health Issue." *Acta Medica Marisiensis* 62, no. 4 (2016): 408–21. https://doi.org/10.1515/amma-2016-0048.

33. "Value." value_1 noun - Definition, pictures, pronunciation and usage notes | Oxford Advanced Learner's Dictionary at OxfordLearnersDictionaries.com. Accessed May 26, 2020. https://www.oxfordlearnersdictionaries.com/us/definition/english/value_1?q=value.

34. Shetty, Jay. *Think like a Monk: Train Your Mind for Peace and Purpose Every Day*. New York: Simon & Schuster, 2020.

35. Alexander, Elizabeth M., and Linda McMullen. "Constructions of Motherhood and Fatherhood in Newspaper Articles on Maternal and Paternal Postpartum Depression." *Gender and Language* 9, no. 2 (2014): 143–66. https://doi.org/10.1558/genl.v9i2.17318

36. Frankhouser, Tara Lynn, and Nicole L. Defenbaugh. "An Autoethnographic Examination of Postpartum Depression." *The Annals of Family Medicine* 15, no. 6 (2017): 540–45. https://doi.org/10.1370/afm.2107.

37. Rubin, Gretchen. *Happiness Project*. New York: HarperCollins Publishers, 2018.

38. Manson, Mark. *The Subtle Art of Not Giving a Fu*k: a Counterintuitive Approach to Living a Good Life*. New York: HarperOne, an imprint of HarperCollins Publishers, 2016.

39. Frankhouser, Tara Lynn, and Nicole L. Defenbaugh. "An Autoethnographic Examination of Postpartum Depression." *The Annals of Family Medicine* 15, no. 6 (2017): 540–45. https://doi.org/10.1370/afm.2107

40. Phillips, Sally, and Lesley Pitt. "Maternal Mental Health: Making a Difference." *Aotearoa New Zealand Social Work* 23, no. 3 (2016): 31–37. https://doi.org/10.11157/anzswj-vol23iss3id158.

41. Phillips, Sally, and Lesley Pitt. "Maternal Mental Health: Making a Difference." *Aotearoa New Zealand Social Work* 23, no. 3 (2016): 31–37. https://doi.org/10.11157/anzswj-vol23iss3id158.

42. "Impostor Syndrome: Symptoms, Types, and How to Deal with It." Medical News Today. MediLexicon International

(2020). https://www.medicalnewstoday.com/articles/321730#symptoms.

43. Shetty, Jay. *Think like a Monk: Train Your Mind for Peace and Purpose Every Day*. New York: Simon & Schuster, 2020.

44. Krasnova, Hanna, Thomas Widjaja, Peter Buxmann, Helena Wenninger, and Izak Benbasat. "Research Note—Why Following Friends Can Hurt You: An Exploratory Investigation of the Effects of Envy on Social Networking Sites among College-Age Users." *Information Systems Research* 26, no. 3 (2015): 585–605. https://doi.org/10.1287/isre.2015.0588.

45. Kendall-Tackett, Kathleen. "Birth Trauma: The Causes and Consequences of Childbirth-Related PTSD." Praeclarus Press, June 4, 2021.

46. Quintero, Samara, and Jamie Long. "Toxic Positivity: The Dark Side of Positive Vibes." The Psychology Group Fort Lauderdale, March 12, 2021. https://thepsychologygroup.com/toxic-positivity/.

47. David, Susan. *Emotional Agility.* Penguin USA, 2018.

48. David, Susan. *Emotional Agility.* Penguin USA, 2018.

49. Clear, James. "The Ivy Lee Method: The Daily Routine for Peak Productivity." James Clear, February 4, 2020. https://jamesclear.com/ivy-lee.

50. Covey, Stephen. *First Things First,* 1994.

51. Shetty, Jay. *Think like a Monk: Train Your Mind for Peace and Purpose Every Day.* New York: Simon & Schuster, 2020.

52. Zayfert, Claudia, and Jason C. DeViva. *When Someone You Love Suffers from Posttraumatic Stress: What to Expect and What You Can Do.* New York, NY: Guilford, 2011.

53. Buettner, Dan. "Hara Hachi Bu: Enjoy Food and Lose Weight With This Simple Japanese Phrase." Blue Zones. Blue Zones, June 2, 2020. https://www.bluezones.com/2017/12/hara-hachi-bu-enjoy-food-and-lose-weight-with-this-simple-phrase/.

54. Dennis, Cindy-Lee, and Lori Ross. "Relationships Among Infant Sleep Patterns, Maternal Fatigue, and Development of Depressive Symptomatology." *Birth* 32, no. 3 (2005): 187–93. https://doi.org/10.1111/j.0730-7659.2005.00368.x.

55. Daaloul, Houda, Nizar Souissi, and Damien Davenne. "Effects of Napping on Alertness, Cognitive, and Physical Outcomes of Karate Athletes." *Medicine & Science in Sports & Exercise* 51, no. 2 (2019): 338–45. https://doi.org/10.1249/mss.0000000000001786.

56. Kendall-Tackett, Kathleen. "Birth Trauma: The Causes and Consequences of Childbirth-Related PTSD." Praeclarus Press, June 4, 2021.

57. Lindberg, Sara. "Postpartum Diet Plan: Tips for Healthy Eating After Giving Birth." Healthline. Healthline Media, July 31, 2020. https://www.healthline.com/health/postpartum-diet.

58. Shetty, Jay. *Think like a Monk: Train Your Mind for Peace and Purpose Every Day.* New York: Simon & Schuster, 2020.

59. Shetty, Jay. *Think like a Monk: Train Your Mind for Peace and Purpose Every Day.* New York: Simon & Schuster, 2020.

60. Kendall-Tackett, Kathleen. "Birth Trauma: The Causes and Consequences of Childbirth-Related PTSD." Praeclarus Press, June 4, 2021.

61. "Reproductive Mental Health." Signs & Symptoms | Reproductive Mental Health: Supporting BC women's mental health before, during and after pregnancy. Accessed June 7, 2020. https://reproductivementalhealth.ca/psychosis/signs-symptoms.

62. "Reproductive Mental Health." Panic Disorder | Reproductive Mental Health: Supporting BC women's mental health before, during and after pregnancy. Accessed June 7, 2020. https://reproductivementalhealth.ca/anxiety/panic-disorder.

63. "Reproductive Mental Health." OCD | Reproductive Mental Health: Supporting BC women's mental health before, during and after pregnancy. Accessed June 7, 2020. https://reproductivementalhealth.ca/anxiety/ocd.

64. "Reproductive Mental Health." PTSD | Reproductive Mental Health: Supporting BC women's mental health before, during and after pregnancy. Accessed June 7, 2020. https://reproductivementalhealth.ca/anxiety/ptsd.

Manufactured by Amazon.ca
Bolton, ON

21670567R00136